"Do you bring in a lamp to put it under
a bowl or a bed?
Instead, don't you put it on a stand?
For whatever is hidden is meant to be disclosed,
and whatever is concealed is meant to be brought
out into the open.
If anyone has ears to hear, let him hear."

Mark 4:21-23
NIV

Reviewers Comments...

"An excellent and outstanding job ! Wonderful information and very powerful case presentation."
- Dr. Ann Parsons, Chiropractic Physician, Nutrition Specialist

"Great job! Well done on the chemical section. Not easy to do without giving chemistry lessons. Now all you have to do is begin to educate people about the cumulative affects of these materials and what it can do to them."
– S. Brett DeLawter, D.D.S.

"I found the information in this book to be very interesting and very informative. A must read for anyone who cares about their personal safety."
– Linda Rios-Beers, Registered Dental Assistant

"The information Lisa Ann has given in her book is not only timely, it is powerful! If you have ever had manicures, pedicures or acrylic nails, you owe it to yourself to read this book!"
- Krista, Emergency Room Nurse

"A Pandora's box full of facts that will shock you – A must read for anyone who has their nails done."
– Tricia Coffman

"This book has empowered me with information and confidence with which I can now make informed decisions about not only my own nail care, but that of people I love."
– Robin S., Health Care Professional

"As I read Lisa's book, a quote from my favorite movie, The Wizard of Oz, came to mind: "Oh, what a world, what a world. Who would have thought just <u>one girl</u> could have destroyed all my beautiful wickedness." Bless you Lisa, for being that <u>one woman</u> who cared enough to stand on our behalf, and educate us about the "beautiful wickedness" in the nail care industry."
– Debra Smith, Realtor

nail care nightmares
The truth behind the beauty

A guide to public awareness

Lisa Ann Bowles

First Edition

HEALMB PUBLISHING®

Clovis, California

Nail Care Nightmares; The Truth Behind the Beauty
A Guide to Public Awareness
by Lisa Ann Bowles

PUBLISHING ®

1466 Clovis Avenue
Clovis, California 93612 U.S.A.

Copyright © 2007 Lisa Ann Bowles
Copyright © 2013 Lisa Ann Bowles

ISBN-10: 0-9788243-7-7
ISBN-13: 978-0-9788243-7-2
First Edition 2007
Second Edition 2013
Printed in the United States of America

2006938553

In Memory Of My Loved Ones

My mother, *Elvira R. Lopez*   1939-2006
My stepfather, *Victor A. Lopez*   1928-1999
My father, *Arthur H. Bowen*
My father-in-law, *Brinton N. Bowles*   1908-1993
My grandfather, *Vern O. Woodward*   1901-1982
My grandmother, *Mildred J. Woodward*
1911-1980

DEDICATION

This book is dedicated to my mother,

Elvira R. Lopez

My mother was a woman of honesty, integrity, love, compassion and simplicity. Her greatest treasure was her love for GOD, her children, grandchildren and her family.

Her mission in life was to love and be loved. She completed her mission with great success.

1939-2006

CONTENTS

A Word from the Author

Nail Care Nightmares; The Truth Behind the Beauty, is an accumulation of over 20 years experience working as a California Licensed Cosmetologist/Nail Care specialist. This book contains basic information about nail care and information vital to anyone interested in public health and safety. I have worked with ABC, CBS, NBC, Fox News, and various other forms of the media, reporting on sanitation issues and chemicals used to make acrylic nails. While working with reporters, I have been quite surprised to see how much the nail care industry lacks regulation in so many areas. I have met a lot of people along the way and have learned a great deal from them. Much of this knowledge is positive. However, there has to be a balance, and what I have learned from a few of these people is neither positive nor good. Two individuals in particular, who are very well known in the nail care industry, told me I should, *"Keep my mouth shut, do nails, and make my money because nobody really cares about the chemicals that are being used on them."* They also said that I,..."*would never make a difference and nothing would ever change.*"

If I were the only one concerned about the lack of appropriate education and training in this industry, I guess I would have to agree with their statements. Fortunately, I am not the only one who cares. Many of you care and it is for you that I have written this book. As you read this book, no matter where you are in your life or what your occupation, read as it is intended, to educate and bring awareness to this topic. At no time has it been my intention to bash the nail care industry or anyone involved in it. It is my desire to educate and experience a re-generation in this field.

The nail care industry consistently grosses nearly six billion dollars per year. This industry is so great due in part to services and products being sold to the public. As wonderful as that figure is for the industry itself, my question remains, *"Should anyone be making money at the risk of harm or injury to another?"*

The nail care industry has become inundated with hundreds of thousands of manicurists and nail technicians. Unfortunately, many of these individuals cut corners with the products they use and on their methods of sanitation before, during, and after performing a nail care service. There is also an alarming number who are practicing *without* a valid nail technician license. Although the industry generates a large sum of money, its level of professionalism is beginning to plummet. I believe if the public becomes aware of what is going on and if nail technicians make a greater effort to become well trained and informed about the products they are using, the nail care industry will surely regain strength.

So, to the public I say, *"Become aware of the products which are being used on you and of appropriate sanitation procedures."*

If a technician is taking shortcuts it can be VERY DANGEROUS, even life-threatening for you and for the nail technician.

It is my wish that you welcome this information and use it for your greater good. Regardless of whether you accept it or not, I welcome all of your comments and questions. Please address them to:

HEALMB Publishing ®
Attention: Lisa Ann Bowles
1466 Clovis Avenue
Clovis, California 93612

or
Email me at: **nailcarenightmares@gmail.com**
Respectfully,

Lisa Ann Bowles

Acknowledgements

This is where an author recognizes and gives thanks to those who were helpful in the production of their work.

The fact is, since I began this journey in 1997, GOD has allowed hundreds of you to cross my path. Most of the people I have met have been placed in my life for encouragement. Some were placed in my life as roadblocks forcing me to go a different direction or as hurdles, forcing me to jump higher. I thank every one of you for your purpose in my life.

More than *anyone*, more than *anything*, I Thank *GOD* for calling me to the task of writing this book and for being with me *every* step of the way.

Warning and Disclaimer

Because we live in an era which is sue happy, I am forced to write and include the following statement.

This book was written with the intention of informing the public of the potential dangers found within the nail care industry.

Be advised that the information given in this book is for educational purposes only. Be advised also that the information given in this book does not and will not guarantee nor exclude you from harm, illness, danger or any other problem that may arise from allowing a nail technician to perform manicures, pedicures, or artificial nail care services on you.

Every effort has been made to make sure all of the information in this book is accurate and current as of the printing date.

The author and HEALMB Publishing® will not be held liable or responsible to any person or persons, nor to any entity for any reason as a result of information given in this book. For those who will be placing every word in this book under a magnifying glass, you may find mistakes, both typographical and in content.

If you do not agree with the entire statement above and wish not to be bound by it, please do not open this book any further. You may return it immediately for a full refund.

SPECIAL POINT OF INTEREST

For those of you who reside in Connecticut or who may visit the state of Connecticut, you should be made aware of the fact that Connecticut, at the time of this publication, does not require mandatory licensing in the area of Nail Technology.

THE PROBLEMS

As I have mentioned in the previous pages, the nail care industry is grossly under regulated and in desperate need of being cleaned up.

In the following chapters, you will find out what has happened to unsuspecting clients such as yourself. In the final chapters, you will discover how you can protect yourself from becoming a victim of a careless nail technician.

Chapter 1

Pregnancy and Acrylic Nails

In 1997 I began educating nail technicians and the public regarding chemicals used in the nail care industry. Since then one question I have been asked numerous times is, "I am pregnant; can the chemicals used to make acrylic nails harm my unborn baby?" The operative word being "CAN", the answer is yes. YES, the chemicals used to create acrylic nails "CAN" harm your unborn baby. Any answer other than "YES THEY CAN" has in my opinion, been given in complete and total dishonesty or out of plain ignorance.

The reason being, according to the Material Safety Data Sheet (MSDS) for Ethyl Methacrylate (EMA) or Methyl Methacrylate (MMA) monomer (acrylic nail liquid) over exposure to these chemicals "CAN" cause Central Nervous System Depression. The routes of entry of EMA and MMA monomer are inhalation, cutaneous absorption and ingestion (possible if food and drink are nearby). Knowing that the Central Nervous System consists of the brain and spinal cord, we would need to define what Central Nervous System depression is, and we will in a moment. For those who have their nails done or for those who do nails, think about this. When you have your nails done or are creating acrylic nails and the acrylic nail service has been completed, are you able to stand up and walk away? Yes, you can walk away (that is if you walked in). So, if you can walk away then it stands to reason the chemicals that were used to create the acrylic nails did not depress the function of the spinal cord which is what sends messages to your Peripheral Nervous System enabling you to walk. Therefore, depression of the brain function is what we must consider.

While living in Utah, I attended the Utah College of Massage Therapy (UCMT) and the Myotherapy School of Massage. My anatomy instructor at U.C.M.T. was Mr. Mark Nielsen. Mr. Nielsen is not only an instructor at UCMT, he is also a lecturer/professor in the Department of Biology at the

University of Utah. One of the many tools Mr. Nielsen used to teach his students was the opportunity to go to the cadaver lab. My first visit to the cadaver lab brought on a mild anxiety attack, but I quickly arrived at the understanding that we had been given an awesome learning experience by being able to view the human anatomy. I was able to see first hand what the inside of the body, skull and brain looks like. It was fascinating. It was when we studied the brain that I was most intrigued. After seeing and learning what I had, I could really understand how the chemicals, which are used to create acrylic nails, "CAN" affect our Central Nervous System.

We already know that we can walk after an acrylic nail service has been completed. So EMA and MMA monomers do not cause spinal cord depression, right? Therefore, what remains is depression of the brain. In order for the chemicals which are used to create acrylic nails to be able to depress the brain function, the chemicals have to pass through the blood brain barrier. The blood brain barrier consists of blood vessels running through the brain. These blood vessels are different than those in most parts of the body in that the smallest vessels running through the body are porous. The cells of the vessels in the brain are joined together with tight junctions and the cells that are seated next to them are almost fused together. We are created this way in order to keep the brain safe from most of the chemicals we are around, or ingest daily. However, substances with smaller molecules such as oxygen, alcohol and anesthetics can easily cross the blood brain barrier. This is the reason our brain gets the oxygen it needs, you can be put to sleep for a surgery, or can become intoxicated when you consume too much alcohol. Now you know what portion of the Central Nervous System "CAN" be affected by these chemicals. Let's take a look at the definition of depression.

A brief definition of **depression** is; **to depress, to lower, a feeling of sadness, an emotional inability to concentrate or to think clearly**.

In order to detect Central Nervous System Depression, we need to know what the signs are and how it affects the body. Signs and symptoms include, but are not limited to; fatigue, loss of concentration and confusion. Before you would show signs and symptoms in the Central Nervous System, the chemicals must reach the brain matter and affect the portion of the brain which controls such things as fatigue, loss of concentration and confusion. The portions of the brain which control this can be found in the frontal lobe, or more specifically the prefrontal area, which is concerned with the intellectual activities.

The brain is also where many critical glands are found. For instance, the Pituitary Gland, also known as the master gland, and is approximately about the size of a pea. This gland is responsible for producing many of the hormones that regulate many body functions. The Pituitary Gland has an Anterior and a Posterior lobe. The Anterior lobe is responsible for providing hormones that protect the body in stressful situations, stimulates the thyroid to produce thyroxin, stimulates growth and hormone activities of ovarian follicles, stimulates growth of the testes which promotes development of sperm, promotes growth of all body tissue and causes development of corpus luteum which produces estrogen and progesterone.

The Posterior Pituitary is responsible for providing hormones which promote proper function of the kidneys and stimulates smooth muscle tissue of the blood vessels. It also causes contractions of the uterus in pregnant women and ejection of milk from the mammary glands. Having said this, the chemicals which are used to create acrylic nails, "CAN" harm your unborn baby by causing either a depletion of excitatory neurotransmitters or blockage of the same, possible by the excitation of depressive neural pathways in the brain.

Depression of the brain functions can cause a cascade effect which may depress functions downstream from the brain including necessary functions having to do with the progression of pregnancy. This last statement, at the present time, is inadequately studied. However, neurological deficits found in unborn fetus' "CAN" reasonably be assumed both, from direct affects of the acrylic monomers (all inclusive) on the fetus, as well as downstream effects from the mother.

For those of you who are having a difficult time believing this statement, please remember there was a time when it was said that smoking cigarettes and drinking alcohol, while pregnant, were perfectly safe and would not cause harm to a fetus. Common sense, time, research and testing has shown us, **beyond the shadow of a doubt** smoking cigarettes "CAN" and in fact DOES cause cancer and also causes harm to a fetus. Medical research has also proven **beyond the shadow of a doubt,** drinking alcohol while pregnant "CAN" and DOES cause Fetal Alcohol Syndrome (FAS). A few of the effects of FAS may be; physical abnormalities, attention difficulty, mental retardation, physical disabilities and memory difficulty. So, perhaps it would be more appropriate to use the word "WILL" instead of "CAN". Such as, "Will the chemicals used to create my beautiful acrylic nails harm my unborn baby?" Upon posing the question with the word "WILL", the answer must then be, "This is an area which is unclear and has not had enough study and research to be able to give a definitive answer." This is what we are currently being told anyway.

Keep in mind, cigarettes and their ability to cause cancer and consuming alcohol while pregnant and its ability to cause Fetal Alcohol Syndrome had to be researched, studied, tested and documented at great length before scientific conclusions were drawn and given to the public. I have also heard others responding to this question with answers such as, *"I had my nails done with acrylic products during my entire pregnancy and my baby is perfectly fine* and *I did acrylic nails all day long and my baby is perfectly fine with 10 fingers and 10 toes"*. What I have to say to this is; not always does an adverse condition show up physically. There is a chance that something could be wrong neurologically. I believe the truth will be revealed much the same as was the exposure of the hazards of smoking cigarettes and drinking alcohol while pregnant.

The ball is already rolling in the political arena in regard to the cosmetic industry and issues with chemicals used to make cosmetics (all inclusive). For those of you who are pregnant or who want to become pregnant, please study this area thoroughly. Artificial nails are not worth the possible risks of being exposed to questionable chemicals that may harm your baby.

Chapter 2

Acetone Explosion

It was March of 2001; I had just received the April 2001 edition of NAILS Magazine, a well known trade magazine. As I read the magazine, I came across an article about a nail technician who experienced an acetone accident. The article stated that on January 9, 2001, a nail technician was heating acetone in a glass bowl in the salon microwave, when the acetone ignited. It goes on to say, "The pressure blew open the door of the microwave and engulfed the nail technician in flames," and that she, "..ran from the salon with her face, hair and clothing on fire." Other's in the salon were able to extinguish the flames but not before the victim had suffered third degree burns over 15% of her body. A number of employees in the salon told the fire department the heating of acetone in the microwave was a common practice. It seems this is common throughout the United States. The reason nail technicians do this is because warm acetone helps remove acrylic nails quickly. While this is a true statement, heating acetone in the microwave should NEVER be done. The article ended by stating that the nail technician was in critical condition and heavily sedated.

After reading the article, I had a gnawing feeling there was more to the story, so I began to search for this person in hopes of asking her what really happened. On Saturday, June 16, 2001, Debbie Greenwood returned a phone call I had made to her. In what follows, Debbie tells *her* story in *her* own words, of events leading up to, and following the incident.

"My name is Debra Greenwood. I am a nail technician and shop owner from Knoxville, Tennessee. I have owned my shop for over ten years. It is located in a very busy area of the Knoxville business district. It was the first time in my life that I could ever really make a statement like that and actually mean what I was saying. I was 49 years old and was feeling pretty happy with myself and my life when, in a flash of a second,

my life was turned upside down. In January of 2001, I had a very serious accident occur in my salon. I had several particular people working with me and at some point they began heating acetone in the microwave. Heating acetone helped to remove the acrylic nails more easily and quickly. At some point, I remarked I did not think it was a very good idea because acetone is flammable, but I was blown off as being silly and told it was fine for acetone to be heated for just 10-15 seconds. I do not remember when I finally jumped on the bandwagon and began heating the substance, but on January 9, 2001, I overheated about one inch of acetone in a small glass dish. After about twenty seconds of heating, I realized the acetone had been in the microwave a long time. I glanced at it and saw the chemical was dancing in the bowl. I reached over and turned the microwave off then continued to allow it to stand for about forty five seconds longer. Finally, I opened the door, and it appeared to be fine. I reached inside the microwave and set it out. It was still alright.

Someone from out in the shop spoke to me and I took a step toward the door to an-

swer them. As I took that step, the acetone made a small little poof and ignited. It was probably a matter of three seconds or so before I realized I was on fire. I screamed for help and stepped about three steps over to the sink where I immediately stuck my head under water. Two of my co-workers ran to my rescue and wrapped a coat around me, smothering the fire. I was on fire less than two minutes, but suffered first degree burns all over my face and third degree burns on my right hand, arm and leg. The actual ignition of the fire was caused by the vapor of the acetone after heating. The static electricity from the carpet created the spark to start the fire. It was a very freaky accident, but one that brought forth a wide awakening for myself as well as many people. I was taken to the local hospital, which is a teaching hospital and trauma unit for the Knoxville area.

The ambulance ride was nine minutes and thirty two seconds and was a period of excruciating pain. I was taken into UT Hospital and was there less than one hour total time, when they told me I was being taken by Lifestar Helicopter to the Vanderbilt Burn

Center in Nashville which was one and a half hours away. My family had arrived, I was doing fair but the pain was unbearable. Before we left UT Hospital, I was put to sleep for a matter of minutes and a tube was inserted down my throat in case I began to swell, which is common in burn patients. Minutes later, I was awakened and felt myself being rolled onto rough pavement. I could hear the engine of the helicopter as my sister was rubbing my foot. Since her husband is a mechanic for Lifestar, and knew many of the male nurses who would be attending to me, she said to me, "Just hang tough and don't panic, these guys are going to take good care of you." As they shuffled me into the noisy helicopter, I noticed I could not open my eyes and I could not move any of my body parts. Until now, I had managed to remain very calm the entire time and had answered all of their questions regarding personal information, but now I was beginning to feel nervous. My daughter was there, and I knew when I saw her face, I was a mess. I literally saw her stop in her tracks and force a stoic brave expression on her face, before she walked into the room with her business partner.

By the look on her face and in spite of her expression, I knew it was bad, so I tried to lighten the severity of my condition remarking to her I thought I had really done a number on myself. She never said much of anything to me but listened intently while the doctors paraded around my bed. As I was lying in the helicopter, I couldn't concentrate very well and kept remembering her expression. The pain was unbelievable. I heard the male nurses discussing my condition. I was already on an IV drip of morphine and they emphasized the fact that it was a pretty high dosage. I had been given a paralyzing drug to prevent me from moving or pulling any tubes out. I kept trying to move my hand or foot to let them know I could hear them, but nothing moved. It was probably ten minutes into the flight when I began to think the pain was going to kill me. At that moment, I began to pray, "Lord, if I have ever done anything right in my life, please Lord, just please, let me sleep." I slipped into a coma immediately after that prayer.

My arrival at Vanderbilt Hospital was routine from what I understand. I was ad-

mitted to the Burn Intensive Care Unit. My closest girlfriend, Jennifer Thomas, followed close behind and my family all came the next morning. They had talked with the head of the Burn Center. He had told them to come prepared to stay for at least a couple of weeks, but most likely longer. Jennifer and one of the attending nurses informed me later I was semi-conscious after I arrived at Vanderbilt and I communicated very effectively with both of them. I have no memory of that process. By 8:00 the following morning my parents had arrived. I communicated with my mom and asked her to call a friend. Shortly after that point in time, I went into a full coma.

It was during this comatose state that I became very ill. The first complication started with a very severe case of pneumonia, followed by ARDS (Acute Respiratory Distress Syndrome) which brought about extreme breathing problems. At some point, the process of de-breeding my burned skin had begun and then I began to swell. I do not really know at what point they did all my skin grafts, but all of the skin was stripped from my breast to my pelvic area and was grafted to my hand, arm and leg. Everyday or so the *doctor would tell my parents he thought he would have to do a tracheotomy because it would make my breathing easier. The only reason he had held off from doing the surgery was because my body had become so frail he did not think I would survive.*

I began to swell, my kidneys were not functioning. I grew larger and larger within hours and began to look like a monster. Many of my friends were driving to Nashville to see me, almost on a daily basis and my parents gave up their family time to accommodate them. I evidently looked so bad a couple of them almost fainted. My bottom lip was swollen down under my chin. I had no eyes and the skin had begun to split open. I was absolutely huge. A yellow pus-like substance was seeping from my mouth, nose, eyes and ears. It was the pneumonia being expelled from my body. Soon after, my white blood count tripled. Within a couple of hours an infection had started. They began to give me some fancy antibiotic that did not touch the infection for four days. Finally, they located where it was coming from. It was not an infection from the burns, but a vaginal abscess, a result of lying in a coma for such a long period of time.

Soon there were signs the infection was under control, but my kidney function had worsened significantly, I was now in danger of losing my life. This was the second time they thought I might not make it. Everything had been completed at this time. All of the surgery was finished and now it was just a waiting game. Many prayers were said for both my life and a full recovery. My doctor was Dr. Jeffrey Guy, head of the Burn Center, and an amazing doctor possessing a wonderful bedside manner. He spent about an hour with my family on a daily basis answering questions, calming their fears and helping to prepare them for what could have been the worst. The entire Burn Center staff was unbelievably good to my family, portraying an expert level of care that would be a major challenge for any other staff or hospital to achieve anywhere in the world.

I began to awaken and as I came back to a conscious state, I looked around me only to realize that I did not know where I was. As I assessed myself and my surroundings, I remembered the accident. I have no memory of talking to anyone before I awoke until my mother walked into the room. I was trying to talk to her but could only whisper. I thought I had been there overnight and was astonished when she told me I had been in a coma for 24 days. I tried to focus on what I was being told, but I still had absolutely no memory of what had happened. Later, my daughter told me they had given me an amnesia drug which prevented me from remembering anything.

According to the stories I have been told, that was just one of many blessings that came my way. Although I was still being given very heavy drugs, I had to focus on trying to walk again, swallowing and learning to do all kinds of things I used to do but had now forgotten to do. My muscles had not worked for so long I had to start over with most things. My tongue was burned and I had numbness around my lips and inside my mouth. I could not feel the fork on my lips as my mouth was drooling the food and liquid. I was not able to hold my fork and steer my food to my mouth. Nothing worked quite the same as before and all of the things a person takes for granted were a challenge for me.

One of the things I can remember very vividly as having a profound effect on me took place on the second day I was awake. I asked if I could take a shower and was told I was too weak so a nurse offered to help me. We went down the hall to a bathroom and she put a chair in the tub. Using a handheld shower nozzle, she helped me bathe. I cried like a baby because the water felt so good flowing down on my body and what a tremendous feeling it was to wash my hair and be clean again. Every day I asked when I could go home. I was worried about my business and all my family had been through. My daughter had taken over the running of my business and was driving back and forth to Nashville two to three times a week. She was striving to keep everything going for me.

My father, who has been very ill for several years was holding up well, but I was worried about him and needed to go home for him, for my family and for me. I continued to ask when I could go back to Knoxville and was told I would have to go to rehabilitation, which was upstairs on the seventh floor. I was devastated but knew I had to do it.

The therapists kept a hot trail to my room all day long, telling me I had to exercise my hand or I would lose the use of it. I had to walk as often as possible to regain my strength. I had lost 68% of my muscle mass from lying in the coma and was weak as a kitten. My first walk down the hall was about twenty feet with the help of a walker, my mother, and a nurse. Three days later, I was walking the full length of the hall with no help. Six days after coming out of the coma, Dr. Guy when making his morning rounds was astonished when he saw me and jumped around the room. I was elated when he said I could go home. I was walking out of the hospital and going home, not a rehabilitation center, but home to Knoxville. Hundreds of prayers had been answered.

I arrived at my front door that night and was so happy to see my house. I had been told enough stories by this time to know I was one lucky lady and had been blessed in so many different ways. The next several weeks were very difficult, but I was determined to be back to normal as soon as possible. I pushed myself, probably too hard at times, but I did it just the same. My parents alternated with *my daughter and both of my sisters, staying with me around the clock for three weeks. I had therapy three times a week.*

On the day I arrived home, I asked my mother to take me to my shop. I went every day except two, and stayed for a limited amount of time. My family had been told I would not work for 8-10 months. During my fifth week at home, I went back to work and stayed for about 4-6 hours. I did well but was totally exhausted when I got home. During the five weeks I was recovering, I totally redecorated my salon, which gave me something positive to focus on. In June of 2001, I worked from noon to 7:00 p.m. every day. I was in therapy five days a week and have regained 70% of the total use of my hand. Since my fifth week out of the hospital, I was not just working in my salon doing administrative duties I was also doing nails every day.

It is so extremely important to remain positive for all endeavors in your life. I think it has been a strong positive attitude that helped me to recover as well as I have, along with an excellent medical staff, and of course answers to tons of prayers. There have been *countless blessings as a result of this accident. I had no insurance and my hospital bills peaked to about $311,000. A medical fund was set up on my behalf. When I returned home from the hospital, I watched it grow and it is still continuing to grow.*

I have some friends in Mexico who even organized a benefit which raised $2,500.00. I had offers to clean my house and business, chauffeur me anywhere I needed to go, prepare meals for me and countless other wonderful extensions of love.

There are many things I have left out of this story, but I am happy to have the opportunity to share my experience with others. I only wish that every nail technician would read this book so they can be reminded of how important it is to be mindful of what you are doing everyday. These are dangerous chemicals we work with and we need to treat them with respect. I think one thing I have also realized is we are not properly educated (at least in the state of Tennessee) as to how dangerous these chemicals are and how they need to be handled. I had college chemistry so I knew the dangers, but still did not remain mindful of my actions.

If I can tell my story and prevent one person from having an injury of this nature, then telling my story and reliving the painful recovery has all been worth it for me. I was so fortunate not to lose my eyesight or to be terribly deformed. My hand and arm will be scarred forever, but my face is very close to perfect. As a matter of fact, the doctor told me I had a very expensive face-lift, which was another one of those blessings.

In closing I would like to thank all of the wonderful people who have so generously given their time to help me in so many ways and I thank you, Lisa, for sharing your book with me so I can tell my story."

Debbie, a professional nail technician, has been gracious enough to share her story with us. I hope you will take it to heart as a member of the public and speak out when you have been placed in a dangerous situation involving highly flammable chemicals. What happened to Debbie *can* happen to you. Be mindful also that you should speak up if you see a candle burning in a beauty establishment. There have been reports of clients catching on fire because their technician had a candle burning near their work station. I talked to firefighter, **Pablo Flores** of the **Los Angeles Fire Department** in California about burning candles around chemicals, here is what he had to say:

Question: Pablo, do you see any problems with burning candles in a salon, spa or nail shop where chemicals are being used?
Answer: Yes. You need to keep the chemicals away from open flame, you can start a fire if you do not. Also, the vapors of chemicals near an open flame can cause combustion.
Question: How about in a home where someone does their own nails?
Answer: The same principles apply. Open flames from candles can react violently with the chemicals from nail products.
Question: Have you ever had to go on a call to a beauty establishment or a home because of someone burning a candle near nail care chemicals?
Answer: Yes. Someone had left a burning candle in the bathroom along with various nail and bath products. The person walked away not extinguishing the candle. The

fumes from the products mixed with the open flame and caught a towel on fire which then burned the counters. The fire was stopped by the resident, but we were still called out to investigate.

Question: As a firefighter, what advice would you give to those who burn candles around volatile chemicals during a nail care service or when they do their own nails at home?

Answer: *Please be careful. At home or at work, do not put candles and chemicals near each other.*

How Percentages and Degrees of Burns are Determined

For those who may not understand the severity of this incident, I have included below some information on how percentages and degrees of how burns are determined. The percentage of the body damage is frequently calculated by using a technique called the *Rule of Nines*. The body is divided into areas of 9% each.

The severity of a burn is determined by how many layers of the tissue have been

The head (each side, front and back)	4.5%
The arms (each arm, front and back)	4.5%
The torso (each side, front and back)	18%
The groin	1%
The legs (each leg, front and back)	9%
Total	100%

affected. The following describes each degree of burn.

- First degree burns (also called partial thickness burn) include mild sunburn. Symptoms include mild pain, some redness, no blisters, surface layers of skin (epidermis) may peel, and minimal skin damage as compared to the other degrees.
- Second degree burns (also called partial thickness burn) involve the entire epidermis and reach the dermis, which consists of sweat glands, hair follicles and sebaceous (oil) glands. Burns of this degree will obviously cause damage but

will not destroy the area.

- Third degree burns (also called full thickness burn) are the most severe of burns. The third degree burn is characterized by the complete destruction of the epidermis and the dermis. In addition, tissue death extends below the primary skin layers into the subcutaneous tissue.

One distinction between second and third degree burns is, third degree lesions are insensitive to pain immediately after injury because of the destruction of nerve endings. The fluid loss that results from third degree burns is a very serious problem. Another serious problem with third degree burns is the greater risk of infection.

Chapter 3

Death Of A Child

Some will say this chapter was created by "document dredging." What they mean by this is, the following information was documented a long time ago. A portion of the information I am about to pass on to you was documented many years ago, however, it is necessary to note such an incident in order to help you understand how long it takes for change to occur within this industry or any other industry for that matter.

A report states, in Los Angeles, California in 1987, a 16-month-old died of cyanide poisoning after swallowing a product that was used for removing artificial nails. The product in question was "Acetonitrile", a chemical that when ingested, breaks down into cyanide. The product was packaged in a glass bottle with a screw-on cap. Some of these types of products were purple in color and smelled similar to grapes. This product was a known toxin, a potentially fatal chemical, yet it was in packaging even a small child could open. He did, he ingested it and he died.

The report was written by Dale Blumenthal, a member of the FDA Public Affairs and is entitled, "Artificial Nail Remover Poses Poisoning Risk." The full report was found by logging onto **www. fda.gov** and then searching for "Cyanide Death". There is more information in the report that will be of great interest to many of you, specifically those of you who are using artificial nail care products at home. I am sure many of you are now saying, "Okay this is sad, but come on it's negligible in relation to the bigger picture." Personally, I do not feel that way. I cannot imagine losing my child and I do not feel as though this incident should be swept under the rug as though it is of no importance. There are hundreds of thousands of you who are using artificial nail care products in your home and it is of grave importance you become aware of the dangers of having these chemicals in your home. You must know how to work with them and how to store them appropriately.

For the record, the child mentioned prior is not the only child that has been injured as a result of coming into contact with artificial nail care chemicals. A statement written by Senator Edward Kennedy in 1997, states that over 16,000 children a year are acutely injured as a direct result of artificial nail care products alone.

How, you ask? Here is one example. When I was teaching nail care courses in the state of Utah I met a young lady by the name of Angie. Angie was a nail technician who worked out of her home. During one of our lessons, I was explaining the differences in many of the chemicals a nail technician uses in the course of their day. I began to explain what Methacrylic Acid (MAA, Primer) was and how dangerous it could be if a child got into it. Angie's eyes teared up. I asked her if she was okay. She began to tell me of how her niece had gotten into her acrylic nail supplies and put a bottle of Methacrylic Acid (MAA, Primer) to her mouth ready to drink it. Angie said she reached for her niece just in time to stop her from drinking the primer, but not in time to stop her from putting it onto her lips. Angie said she "freaked out" because as she took the primer bottle away from her niece, she saw smoke coming from her lips. The next day Angie called me and told me she was so bothered by what had happened to her niece, she moved her nail care business from her home into a full service salon.

Due to incidents like these, regulatory agencies now require many chemicals such as primer, to have child resistant packaging and caution statements on the bottles. Although these requirements are in place, it does not mean you would have legal recourse in the event your child was injured because of coming into contact with chemicals you have in your home. Caution statements usually include, "Do Not Ingest", "Keep Away From Children", and "Not for Household Use". The warnings are made very clear. For this reason alone, product manufacturers can be excluded from any and all legal action should your child be injured and should *you* try to take legal action against the manufacturer.

For those who are using artificial nail care chemicals in your home, here are a few tips on how to avoid potential dangers to you and your family.

* Request a Material Safety Date Sheet for the products you are using and read them. This information can be obtained from your beauty supply house. Please see page 89 for information on a MSDS.

* Always open a window when you are working with acrylic liquid (monomer) in

order to reduce your chances of becoming overexposed to the vapors of the liquid.

* Never smoke or burn candles around nail care chemicals such as acrylic liquid, acetone, polish, or polish remover. These chemicals are very volatile and flammable.

* Keep all nail care chemicals out of the reach of children. It is best to store all chemicals in a locked cabinet.

* If you do your own nails at home, do not allow your children to come close to you while you are working with the chemicals.

* If you spill Methacrylic Acid (MAA, Primer) on yourself or anyone else, immediately make a paste mixture of baking soda and water then quickly apply it to the area exposed to the Primer. This will neutralize the chemical action of the acid which will hinder and/or stop possible chemical burning.

Chapter 4

Don't Be Fooled

Okay, so you want to have your nails done. You are not sure where to go or what to do. You have heard "horror" stories from people on the news, on the radio, and you have read articles in the newspaper. When you have finished reading this chapter, you will be able to determine whether or not you are being "fooled" about the type of nail enhancement products that are being used on you. Due to the ongoing media attention certain nail care products have had recently and in years past, more and more manufacturers are promoting "new" products and new ways of applying them.

Currently the most popular is the "gel" nail. Unfortunately, there are thousands of manicurists who may be fooling you into having "gel" nails applied when in fact what you are getting are acrylic nails (usually Methyl Methacrylate based) topped with a "gel" sealant. Many of you are gladly paying a higher price for these "gel" nails believing they are better or safer than acrylics, when in fact, you are being taken advantage of.

In this chapter, I will help you to understand what a "gel" nail is *NOT*. In the next chapter, I will help you understand what several of the popular types of nail enhancement products are and how they are applied.

"Gel" nails;
There are two types.
1.) One that cures without a light,
2.) One that cures with a UV light.
Typically "gel" products are traditional acrylic liquids and powders premixed for the nail technician.

A true "gel" nail application will consist of applying the "gel"
1.) To the natural nail only,
2.) On top of your natural nail and a plastic tip, which has been glued to your natural nail plate, or
3.) To the natural nail and extended in length by means of sculpting it on top of a form. As the gel product is applied to your

fingernails, your nails will usually be placed under a UV light for the purpose of curing the gel. After all curing is completed, there will be a sticky residue that has to be wiped off. Once this residue has been removed and your technician has refined the overall look of the nails, you should be done.

A true "gel" nail will *NOT* consist of applying an acrylic nail product on your fingernails *first* and then applying a top coat of "gel" over the acrylic nail and curing it. You will know you have had acrylic nails applied first, if the manicurist has taken a brush, dipped it in a liquid and then into a powder and applied it to your fingernails.

If this has happened to you, you can be sure you have been fooled. Additionally, as if that were not enough, the acrylic nail product that was applied to your fingernails may very well be made, in part, with a chemical called *Methyl Methacrylate Monomer*. This is a chemical that has been said by the FDA to be *poisonous and deleterious and is not to be used in the making of acrylic nails*. If you believe you have had this happen to you and you want to test your nails, locate a reputable nail care specialist and ask them to test the product on your nails or you can test it yourself.

To do this test yourself, there are a few things you will need to have. Please see Chapter 6 , *"Test Your Nails"* for details.

Now that you know what a "gel" nail is *NOT*, continue on to the next chapter for information on several of the most popular and widely known artificial nail enhancement products which are available to you, and are being used on you. Learn also how you can test your acrylic nails to see if they are made with chemicals the Food and Drug Administration says are, *"Poisonous and Deleterious."*

Chapter 5

What's On My Nails?

In the previous chapter I explained to you what "Gel" nails were not. Now, I will help you to understand what some of the most popular and widely known artificial nail enhancement products are, what is available to you, and what is being used on your nails. Let's start with acrylic nail products. There are two main types.

ACRYLIC NAILS

METHYL METHACRYLATE (MMA)

This type of acrylic nail product can be found predominantly in what has been known as and said to be, a "discount nail shop" or a "non-standard shop (NSS)."

In some cities you can get a full set of MMA liquid monomer based acrylic nails for as little as ten to fifteen dollars and fills for as little as seven to thirteen dollars. More common though, is to pay about twenty dollars for a full set and fifteen to eighteen dollars for a fill.

If you think your manicurist is using MMA on your nails, ask them. You may get an honest answer and they will admit they are using it. More often than not, you will be told they do not know what they are using or they may tell you they are using OPI. They may say OPI because OPI is a very familiar brand to the public. If you want to test your acrylic nails to see if they are MMA or EMA based, you can follow the suggested guidelines in the next chapter. Information on what Methyl Methacrylate based acrylic nails are, can be found in Chapter 9, *"Chemical Confusion."*

ACRYLIC NAILS

ETHYL METHACRYLATE (EMA)

This type of acrylic nail product is used predominantly by nail technicians who are working in middle or upper end nail salons, either independently or in an establishment with multiple manicurists.

A manicurist using Ethyl Methacrylate liquid monomer based acrylic nail products will generally charge anywhere between twenty and fifty dollars for a full set of acrylic nails. A nail care specialist or nail care artist may charge as much as eighty dollars or more for a full set of nails.

The difference between manicurists, nail technicians and nail artists should be the level of training and experience they have. Often, the difference is no more than a play on words. Remember to look for certificates of training.

If you are not sure what type of acrylic nail product your manicurist is using, ask them. You may also consider asking them if you could see the Material Safety Data Sheet (MSDS). The MSDS will give you an idea of what chemicals the product is made of.

If you want to test your acrylic nails to see if they are MMA or EMA based, as I mentioned earlier, you can follow the suggested guidelines in the next chapter.

Information on what Ethyl Methacrylate based acrylic nails are can be found in Chapter 9, *"Chemical Confusion."*

GEL NAILS

Gel nails are typically traditional acrylic chemicals mixed together for the nail technician and are very sticky. Most of the companies who manufacture gel products put the gel in small jars or pots. Some companies also have colored gels. Gels have become very popular because they usually have very little or no odor. Gels are applied using a step-by-step technique, scooping the gel from the container with a brush and applying it to the nail. After the gel has been applied, it will be introduced to an ultra violet light to begin the curing process. There are chemicals in the gel product called photo initiators that react to the ultra violet light and cause the gel to harden. Gels are more flexible than acrylic nails. If you have had allergic reactions to acrylics, gels *may* be a better choice for you.

However, some individuals who have changed from acrylics to gels because of allergic reactions are beginning to find after time, they react to gel products as well. This could be because gels have a "sticky" layer that must be wiped off with a solvent after the final curing has been completed. If this sticky layer is not wiped off appropriately, allergic reactions are possible. In order to help avoid possible allergic reactions, the nail technician should apply the solvent to a cotton pad, place the cotton pad on the nail enhancement and pull forward. A fresh cotton pad should be used for each nail enhancement. The sticky residue is actually called a "*inhibition*" layer. The inhibition layer is uncured product that has to be wiped off in order to have a high shine finish. If the inhibition layer and the solvent are mixed together, a completely different chemical action may take place. This is how an allergic reaction can occur and this is why the cotton pad with the solvent should be placed on top of the enhancement and pulled forward. Your technician can *scrub* the enhancement with a clean cotton pad and solvent AFTER the inhibition layer has been wiped off in order to achieve the high shine that should be there (the shine will be there if the product has been appropriately cured).

LOW ODOR/NO ODOR ACRYLICS

This type of acrylic is usually Ethyl Methacrylate liquid monomer (EMA) based and was introduced to the nail care industry because upper-end salons and spas wanted to offer artificial nail enhancement services, but did not want to deal with the smell of traditional acrylic nail products. This type of acrylic did well until clients started having allergic reactions to it. It seemed as though nail technicians were being careless in their application because there was no smell. They thought – no smell, no harm. This could not be further from the truth. The truth is low odor/no odor acrylic nail products must be applied the same way traditional acrylics are applied, according to the manufacturers directions and making sure the acrylic liquid (monomer) does not touch the client's skin.

WRAPS

Wraps usually consists of an adhesive (glue), a material such as silk, linen, fiberglass, or paper, and an accelerator. Wraps are usually a multi-step process consisting of placing adhesive on the nail plate, activating the adhesive with the accelerator, placing a piece of material over the nail and then repeating the adhesive and accelerator steps as directed by the manufacturer. This process can be harmful in and of itself because when the accelerator blends with the adhesive, chemical reactions happen quickly, making the adhesive harden. If this process is not followed correctly you may feel a burning sensation. If a nail technician has not had appropriate training with this type of system, he or she can cause great pain and damage to your natural nail, or worse, loss of the entire nail plate. Caution should be followed by those who have this type of product on their fingernails because a great deal of cyanoacrylate (glue, adhesive) is used in some of these types of applications and many of you are allergic to the adhesive.

ACRYLIC DIP SYSTEMS

This type of system is another way of offering the nail technician a product with no smell. This system is usually done by applying an adhesive to the natural nail, then dipping the nail into an acrylic powder. The proposed advantage is supposed to be an acrylic nail with no smell. Unfortunately, many clients are having allergic reactions to this type of system, because of the amount of adhesive (cyanoacrylate) that is used on the natural nail, much the same as is with some of the wraps mentioned above.

GEL/POWDER MIXTURE

This process is done by applying a gel to the nail, and sprinkling acrylic powder on top of the gel before the gel is cured. This is being done by manicurists in hopes of making their gel product as strong as an acrylic nail.

LIQUID PLASTIC

This type of product is also known as a High Density Polymer; Polycarb and Polycrylic. Several companies offer this type of product and market it as an alternative for those who may be allergic to other products. It is applied the same as a gel, then cured with a UV light. The chemical composition of this type of product is a little different. The manufacturers and distributors of such products claim this product is a custom synthesized blend of plastics. One of the most noticeable differences with several of these products is, if you do not slowly introduce the product to the UV light after it has been applied to your nail, you will feel an unbearable heat spike.

This type of product is usually loaded with photo initiators, which is what causes the product to react with the UV light in order to harden completely.

Some products have such a high content of photo initiators that when the curing process is complete, the finished nail will be shiny.

WORD OF CAUTION:

At least one of the manufacturers of this type of product, at the time of this entry, is known to include a cancer causing chemical in a portion of their nail care system. This chemical is called "*Methylene Chloride*" and is on California's Proposition 65 list, as a known cancer causing chemical.

Some of the manufacturers of these products say they use *Methylene Chloride* in their bonding agents in a *small* percent ratio because this chemical *helps the polymer to bond to the natural nail plate.* If you have this type of product on your nails you may want to call the distributor, supplier or manufacturer directly and ask them if this chemical is in *their* product, in **any** amount.

The reason I suggest you ask if it is present in *any* amount is because the manufacturer may be hiding behind the veil of disclosure. What this means is, if there is not "*too much"* of a *questionable* chemical in the product they are manufacturing, *they may not have to tell you it is in there at all.*

In fact, for those of you who will be questioning the manufacturers, distributors, representatives and manicurists associated with this type of product, do not be surprised if they immediately respond by telling you that their product or the product they use DOES NOT contain this chemical. Ask the person you are talking to if they would be willing to sign a statement noting such. Don't be surprised if they refuse this request. They may also say, "*There is a very tiny amount of this chemical present, but it is so minute that "OSHA" does not regulate it.*" The latter statement is ridiculous in and of itself due to the fact that, at the present time, the entire cosmetic industry is grossly under regulated. Furthermore, in order for a chemical to be found "safe" for use, it must be put through a battery of tests, significant data must be recorded and it must go through the appropriate agencies and powers that be along the way in order to claim it "safe". This is a very timely and costly process that a manufacturer will probably not engage upon unless or until they are forced to.

For those of you who have questions and who will continue to search for more information on this topic, you may want to consider adding Toluene and Dibutyl Phthalates to your quest. These two chemicals are readily found in most brands of nail polish.

Toluene is a known reproductive toxin and Dibutyl Phthalates have recently been found to cause testicular abnormalities in baby boys whose mothers were highly exposed to this chemical during pregnancy.

For information on what has happened in California to cause a stirring in the cosmetic industry, read Chapter 18, *"California, Cosmetics and the Law,"* and remember, no one is going to take care of you better than you will yourself. Ask questions. Ignorance is not bliss. You have the right to know what is being used on you and whether the products being used contain trace amounts, or significant amounts of cancer causing chemicals or reproductive toxins so that you can make an informed and educated decision on whether you want the product used on you or not.

Chapter 6

Test Your Nails

Put your acrylic nails to the test.
If you are unsure about the type of acrylic
nail product your manicurist is using on
you, there are several simple steps you can
take to find out.

CAUTION:

You will need to use acetone for this
test. Make sure to follow the manufacturer's guidelines and read the Material Safety
Data Sheet **before** using acetone. All items
listed can be found at Sally's Beauty Supply or most any other beauty supply.

You will need:
- Acetone – a small bottle
- Dappen dish (small glass dish)
- Orangewood stick
- 100 grit nail file

FYI
If you have a gel sealant on top of your

acrylic nails, you will need to use a 100 grit nail file to remove the sealant first. If you do not remove the gel sealant first, you will most likely not be able to test your acrylic nails because gels typically do not soak off in acetone.

To start the test you will need to pour a small amount of acetone into the dappen dish. You only need enough acetone to cover the acrylic product on one nail.

- Place your nail in the acetone and allow the acrylic nail to soak in the acetone for three to five minutes.
- Using an orangewood stick (or cuticle pusher) begin to scrape away the acrylic.

You will know you have Ethyl Methacrylate based acrylic nails if the acrylic product scrapes away with ease and can be completely removed within minutes, fifteen minutes at the most, if the acrylic is thick. You know you have Methyl Methacrylate based acrylic nails if you scrape at it and it will not come off, or if you scrape it and it is very sticky and will not scrape off easily, or if you scrape it and it is hard as a rock.

In the event you have MMA based

acrylic nails and you want them removed, my professional opinion would be that you search for a qualified professional nail technician/specialist who has been trained in the safe removal of MMA based acrylic nails. Whatever you do, *DO NOT* allow anyone to *pull, rip, nip* or *tear* the acrylic nail off.

One of the most common ways many technicians use to remove an acrylic nail is to shove a plastic nail tip between the acrylic product and the natural nail. *DO NOT* allow *anyone* to do this to you. The end result, more often than not, is a very painful and sometimes bloody mess which again, can lead to natural nail damage and severe infection.

Acrylic nails should be removed with a solvent used specifically for this purpose, possible and easy with EMA based acrylic products. They can also be removed by the use of a drill.

Methyl Methacrylate based acrylic nails can *sometimes* be soaked and scraped off, however, this process will take many hours to complete. Hours of exposure to the chemicals used to remove acrylic nail products could result in mild to severe allergic reaction. Therefore I would suggest you not allow a technician to remove the product on your nails using this method.

Chapter 7

Why The Mask?

If I have heard this question once I have heard it a million times, "Why do they wear a mask when they are doing my nails?" Well, here is your answer. Most technicians wear a mask hoping to protect themselves from the vapors of the acrylic nail liquid (monomer). They know the vapors can be very harmful to their system. What many of them do not know is the little white or blue masks they wear give absolutely no protection against the inhalation of the acrylic nail liquid (monomer) vapors. The molecules in the acrylic nail liquid (monomer) are so small the vapors can penetrate through the mask and enter their system anyway.

Another reason they wear the mask is to keep from breathing in the dust created from working with the acrylic. Wearing a mask for this reason is an excellent idea. Most technicians in the nail care industry do not wear a mask to protect themselves from dust because they choose not to. Additionally, some may wear a mask because they have a disease such as Tuberculosis that could be passed on to you via coughing, sneezing, etc. Many of you have also said, "They were wearing a mask yet they did not give me a mask to wear. What is up with that?" Good question! Next time you have your nails done and you see that your technician is wearing a mask, ask them why they are wearing it, then ask them why they have not given you one to wear also. If they hand you a mask to wear, make sure it has not been worn by someone else. Better yet, if you are going to patronize a nail shop where *you* need to wear a mask, take your own. You might also consider finding somewhere else to have your nails done.

Remember, you are responsible for managing *your* personal health and safety.

Chapter 8

Electric Files, AKA Drills, Sanders Or Grinders

Have you ever been hurt by a manicurist who is using a drill on your nails?

A drill is known in the nail care industry as an electric file, e file or electric hand file. It is better known to the public (unfortunately) as a sander or grinder.

Have you ever been burned? Have you ever been cut?

Have you ever experienced red lines on your nail plate (known as *rings of fire*) after your manicurist has used a drill on your nails?

If you have ever experienced any of these, chances are you have been worked on by a technician who has not had appropriate training, or worse yet, has had *no training* in the use of a drill. Allowing anyone to use a drill on you who does not have appropriate training is like allowing a surgeon to operate on you, though they have never used a scalpel before.

A drill can be a very dangerous tool in the hands of someone who has not been taught how to use one.

Drills are available in a variety of styles and features. For example, I own a drill that goes up to 20,000 RPM's. This means the drill bit is able to turn up to 20,000 rotations per minute. I have a variable speed setting which means I can make my drill go very slow or I can turn it on high and it will go extremely fast. If a person who does not know how to use a drill turns the variable speed controller to high, they could literally cut through the natural nail plate within seconds. This can be very dangerous and possibly life threatening.

For instance, let's pretend you went to see Marci the manicurist who was going to use the drill on your nails. What you do not know is, she did not throw away the sander band she used on her last client which is the same sander band she used on several clients from before that, (a sander band is a small cylinder shaped piece of sandpaper attached to a metal piece, called a mandrel) and now she is going to use the same one on you.

By the way, I think I forget to mention, Marci has not been taught how to use a drill so chances are she may end up cutting you, badly. Don't forget! The sander band Marci wants to use on you , is the same sander band she has used on several of the clients before you and she usually cuts her clients at least once during the service.

It doesn't seem like a big deal, right? I mean, if you get cut, it would probably not be bad enough to need much more than a plastic covering. What if one or more of the previous clients who Marci accidentally cut has a communicable disease such as Hepatitis C?

Did you know the Hepatitis C virus stays active after the blood has dried? According to the Centers for Disease Control (CDC) the Hepatitis C virus stays active anywhere from 16 hours up to 4 days after blood has dried.

The natural course is for you to now ask, *"How do we know if the technician has been trained and how do we know if the drill bit is clean?"* These are questions everyone should ask. One of the easiest ways to know if your manicurist has been appropriately trained in the use of a drill is to ask them. If they say yes, ask them if they have received a certificate for their training. Then, take it a step further and ask them to show you their certificate. I know this sounds a bit extreme, but you are literally taking your life and placing it in the hands of your technician. Let me share with you, the reason why, I would make such a bold statement

In order to protect the privacy of the individuals in this story, their names have been changed.

In 2002, I placed an ad in the Fresno Bee Newspaper. The ad was for a massage therapist. After interviewing a number of massage therapists I met a young lady who had quite a story to tell. We will call her *Betsy*.

Before I began *Betsy's* interview I showed her around the salon. *Betsy* looked toward my bookcase where she saw a rough draft of my book and said, "Did you write that?" "Yes" I replied.

She then began to tell me of an experience her friend *Bobby* had with his sister

Samantha. Betsy said *Bobby's* sister died from having her nails done. Imagine my shock and surprise! The first thing I said was, "What happened and can you prove this?" *Betsy* began to tell me what had happened. *She* said *Bobby's* sister went to a nail shop to have her nails done.

The manicurist who was working on *Samantha* used a drill on her nails and ended up drilling not only through the acrylic product but, straight through the nail plate also causing significant bleeding. *Betsy* said *Samantha* went to the hospital and was treated for the injury. Later, due to a serious infection, *Samantha* went back to the doctor who then gave her an antibiotic to kill the infection. However, the antibiotic was not working and the infection worsened. *Betsy* said the infection was so bad the doctor said the finger must be amputated. *Samantha* refused to let this happen. *Betsy* said the infection continued to spread and *Samantha* was told she would need to have her entire hand amputated. *Samantha* refused to let this happen as well. *Betsy* said, the family had to intervene and take *Samantha*, against her will, to the hospital where she had to have her hand amputated at the wrist. It was said *Samantha* was recovering well but then died suddenly. The cause of death? It seems a blood clot formed and moved to her heart. I asked *Betsy* if she could put me in contact with her friends' family. She did talk to the family but the family declined meeting or talking with me. They said what happened was behind them now, there was nothing anyone could do to bring *Samantha* back and they did not want to relive the horror of what had happened.

What you have just read is horrible. It **should not** have happened. Although I was not able to talk to the family personally, I decided to include this story as it was told to me because my hope is , it will be a catalyst for you to understand the potential dangers of allowing an inexperienced technician to use a drill on you.

Technically, *Samantha* did not die from having her nails done. She died from complications of a blood clot. The point is, she would not have died had she not been injured by a technician who was using a drill, who did not have appropriate training on how to use one or who was being blatantly careless.

The incident I have just shared with

you is obviously a worse case scenario and is not an everyday occurrence. What is an everyday occurrence though, and what happens to many people are, incidents such as the skin around the nail being cut with a drill bit or file or a technician causing "*Rings of Fire*" which are slightly curved red lines found on the natural nail plate and are the result of an overzealous technician who has, once again, not been taught how to use a drill or nail file, filing through so many layers of the natural nail plate they come alarmingly close to filing all the way through it, potentially reaching the nail bed itself, which may cause bleeding, and again lead to infection. So, for those of you who are looking at your nails at this very moment and are seeing red lines, you now know what they are and what causes them.

How do you stop this from happening to you? Question your manicurist and *DO NOT* allow them to use a drill on you unless they can prove they have been trained and certified on how to use a drill correctly.

The nail care industry is becoming more and more aware of the problems in regard to drill education or the lack thereof.

I asked a number of experts in this industry to review this chapter. Initially, they all agreed. However, after several months and a slight revision, (upon their request) they ultimately and collectively decided they wanted nothing to do with my book *unless* I would agree to remove the information of the death of *Samantha* and completely re-write the rest of the chapter giving it a more *"positive spin."* The comments of one of the experts was that I was using *"scare tactics"* to get your attention.

After a great deal of thought, I chose to leave the information as I had originally written it. I simply could not find a way to put a *"positive spin"* on the fact that *someone has died* and so many of you have been hurt by untrained technicians who are using a drill on you.

My position remains the same. *You have the right to know what is happening in order to protect yourself!* As for *"scare tactics"*, my intention is not to scare you but rather to inform you. If this information has scared you, so be it. I would rather you be scared and safe, than ignorant and injured.

Before you allow anyone to use a drill on you, ask the person if they have been taught and certified in the use of the machine. Make sure they are using a new sander band on your nails. A sander band is a round, sandpaper type sleeve that fits over the mandrel and used for removing product from the nails. Sander bands are a one time use item and must be thrown away after use. If the technician is going to use a metal bit on your nails, make sure they have appropriately cleaned and disinfected it. This should be done by:

- Washing the bit with soap and water to remove all matter stuck on it.
- Rinsing in warm water.
- Immersing (completely) in an EPA Registered disinfectant for 10 minutes (or per manufacturers directions).
- Removing from disinfectant, rinsing, drying and placing the bits in a dust free container.

More in depth information on how tools of the trade should be cleaned and disinfected may be found in Chapter 20, *"Clean It Up"*.

Chapter 9

Chemical Confusion

For years now, we have heard how certain chemicals in the nail care industry can be dangerous.

In this chapter I will help you to gain a fundamental understanding of what some of these chemicals may be. At the end of this chapter I will give you the names of several additional chemicals you may want to research in order to gain further knowledge in this area.

Let's start with the most controversial chemical at this time.

METHYL METHACRYLATE MONOMER, MMA:

Methyl Methacrylate monomer (liquid) is made by reacting Methacrylic Acid (MAA, Primer) with Methanol (Methyl Alcohol, a poisonous wood alcohol). When these chemicals are mixed together, the result is a Methyl Methacrylate (MMA) and water mixture. Before the Methyl Methacrylate is packaged and shipped to its designated locations, the byproduct of water is removed. Methyl Methacrylate monomer has been around for a long time and has been used for purposes such as making dentures and as a bone cement for joint replacement surgery. The main uses of Methyl Methacrylate monomer include the making of advertisement signs, lighting fixtures, plumbing fixtures, and latex paints. It is also blended with concrete to make the concrete water-repellent.

Several decades ago, manicurists started mixing Methyl Methacrylate monomer liquid with an acrylic powder to create acrylic nails. Unfortunately, the consumers of this type of acrylic nail product began to have allergic reactions. After numerous complaints from those who had suffered from allergic reaction, the Food and Drug Administration (FDA) stepped in.

On July 3, 1974 after litigation, the District Court in Chicago issued an injunction prohibiting the further manufacturing of a product called "Long Nails" which contained Ethyl Methyl Methacrylate monomer. The FDA considers Ethyl Methyl

Methacrylate monomer to be *"A poisonous and deleterious substance"* which should not be used to make acrylic nails. At the time of this entry, nearly all states in the U.S.A. have either prohibited or banned the use of Methyl Methacrylate monomer liquid in the making of acrylic nails.

As a matter of fact, an organization called the Methacrylate Producers Association, Incorporated, has a report on their website which defines exactly what their position is in regard to manicurists using this chemical as well as other methacrylates used to make acrylic nails. Their website may be found by logging onto **www.mpausa.org**. When you reach their home page, click on, "About the Methacrylates".

Having said this, when *the powers that be* got involved, the more *"reputable"* manufacturers of the acrylic nail products started using Ethyl Methacrylate monomer liquid in place of Methyl Methacrylate monomer liquid. Methyl Methacrylate monomer can cause harm by way of cutaneous absorption, inhalation, and ingestion (possible if food or drink are nearby).

Overexposure to this chemical can cause, but is not limited to:

- Allergic reactions, redness, swelling, blisters
- Dizziness, confusion
- Respiratory damage
- Central Nervous System depression/ damage
- Loss of sensation at the fingertips and possibly the entire finger
- Irritation to the eyes

My feeling is, we are soon going to find out there are many more adverse conditions this particular chemical can cause. Time will tell.

ETHYL METHACRYLATE MONOMER, EMA:

The difference between this monomer (liquid) and Methyl Methacrylate monomer is that Ethyl Methacrylate monomer is made by reacting Methacrylic Acid (MMA, Primer) with Ethanol (Ethyl Alcohol – beverage alcohol).

If you just read how Methyl Methacrylate monomer is made you should have a basic understanding of how EMA is made as well because they are made the same way. However, there is a slight difference between Methyl Methacrylate and Ethyl Methacrylate. The EMA molecule is a slightly larger molecule than the MMA molecule so it may not penetrate the skin as easily as MMA, thus may not cause *as much* harm as MMA can.

The Methacrylate Producers Association, Incorporated, disagrees with the nail care industries abilities to obtain and use this chemical to create acrylic nails. They believe the studies in this area are inadequate and Ethyl Methacrylate monomer may be just as harmful as Methyl Methacrylate monomer.

Overexposure to Ethyl Methacrylate is much the same as Methyl Methacrylate and can also include:

- Sore, dry, scratchy throat
- Headache
- Fatigue
- Runny nose
- Insomnia
- Irritability
- Occupational asthma
- Watery eyes
- Central Nervous System depression

METHACRYLIC ACID, MAA:

"Primer"

This chemical is a known corrosive which can cause permanent damage to the skin and natural nail plate.

Methacrylic Acid is widely known as a *"primer"* used to prepare the natural nail plate for the application of artificial nail care products, acrylics in particular.

Methacrylic Acid (primer) is used to chemically "etch" and dehydrate the nail plate. Overuse of the primer can, and does cause chemical burns which can cause moderate to severe damage to the natural nail and nail bed, and tissue (skin) surrounding the nail plate. Not to mention the damage it can cause if it spills on your skin, or worse, is splashed in your eyes. Enough injuries have occurred and been reported related to this chemical that regulatory agencies now say primer must be packaged in "child-resistant" containers. This regulation is found in the Federal Register, Vol. 64, No. 117, June 18, 1999 and applies to nail primers containing Methacrylic Acid packaged on or after June 19, 2000.

Several additional chemicals you should be aware of and concerned about are listed below but are not limited to:

- Toluene (found in nail polish, also used to make explosives and gasoline, may cause damage to the reproduction system)
- Formaldehyde Resin (found in nail polish, can cause allergic reactions)
- Ethyl Acetate (found in nail polish and nail polish remover, may cause central nervous system difficulties and allergic reactions)
- Dibutyl Phthalates (known to cause harm in infant boys)
- Methylene Chloride (a known cancer causing chemical found in some nail bonding systems. Also used to decaffeinate coffee beans)

Chapter 10

Nurses and Nails, Death In the NICU

Several years ago hospitals and other medical facilities across the country began revising their dress code policies in regard to employees who wore artificial nail care products on their fingernails and those who have long natural nails who also have direct contact with patients.

Why you ask? Well, after speaking with *Mr. Gregg Pullen, Manager of Infection Prevention and Control at Children's Hospital Central California,* I found out it started nearly a decade ago. Over a fifteen month period beginning in 1997, 16 newborn babies died from an outbreak of Pseudomonas aeruginosa in a Neonatal Intensive Care Unit in Oklahoma City, Oklahoma. Studies show that nurses with long nails, natural and those covered with artificial nail care products posed a significant risk factor for acquiring the infection. A portion of the concern is that acrylic nails have a level of porosity and can harbor pathogens.

Due to this outbreak and the significant research conducted prior to and after the outbreak, the Centers for Disease Control (CDC) issued a **Category 1A Recommendation** which states, **ALL** medical professionals providing direct patient care should **NOT** wear artificial nail care products.

A Category 1A Recommendation from the CDC is: *Strongly recommended for implementation and strongly supported by well-designed experimental, clinical or epidemiologic studies.*

For those who have natural nails, a **Category II Recommendation** was issued. A *Category II Recommendation* from the CDC is: *Suggested for implementation and supported by suggestive clinical or epidemiologic studies or a theoretical rationale.*

The *Category II Recommendation* from the CDC is that: *Natural nails should be kept to not more than ¼ inch in length.* In the process of researching this topic, I was supplied with information which I found to be, very disturbing.

I have a hospital report which states a particular hospital had, "...463 hospital acquired infections in a twelve consecutive month time frame with 10 of the 463 resulting in **death**." The report also states, it would be naïve of them (the hospital administration) not to assume some portion of the 463 infections and outbreaks were associated with artificial fingernails.

Having said this, a **Category 1A Recommendation** is the *strongest recommendation* the CDC can give, it is not a direct *command*, as the CDC can not *force* anyone to accept a *recommendation*. Make no mistake though, if the CDC has taken steps leading up to releasing a **Category 1A Recommendation** and the recipients of the *recommendation* do not adhere to it, there may be very serious consequences to those who turn their heads. If a medical facility chooses to not accept the *recommendation*, and an outbreak similar to what happened in Oklahoma occurs, chances are great that the facility will be left on its own to attempt to fight a lawsuit which it would almost certainly lose due, to the fact the medical industry is being strongly guided by the CDC to recognize a potentially deadly situation.

This issue is like so many others. Changes *will* occur. Laws and rules *will* be updated and enforced but not until and **AF-TER,** a significant number of individuals have been injured or have died.

The nail care industry appears to hold a different position and opinion.

Before and during the time the hospitals in the central California area started changing their dress code policies prohibiting the wearing of artificial nail care products, I did the nails of many ladies who are nurses. The ladies who worked at Children's Hospital talked to Mr. Pullen in order to hopefully convince him and other "powers that be" that the product I use, would be acceptable for nurses to wear. Their reasoning? The product I use is not porous and does not lift, when maintained.

The nurses were successful in their efforts to arrange a meeting and I was asked to come to Children's Hospital Central California on June 20, 2002 at 2:00 p.m. to meet with Mr. Pullen and a hospital administrator.

A few short hours before my meeting that day, I called a nail care industry expert from a very large and world wide known nail care product manufacturing company. I had a few questions I knew this person could help me with. As always, this gentleman allowed me to ask questions and he kindly answered them. Then he said he had information he wanted me to take with me to the meeting. He made a call to The American Beauty Association, and asked them to facsimile immediately, a report written by Mr. Edward M. Jackson, PhD, President of Jackson Research Associates, Incorporated. The report is titled *"Setting the Record Straight – Some Hospitals Ban Artificial Nails"*.

I read the report and must say it was informative. The report summarized, says; the infectious outbreak was traced back to two nurses, one with long natural nails and the other with long artificial nails. Knowing this, the recommendations the CDC handed down makes sense. The CDC believes if long nails and artificial nails are prohibited the problems of possible infection would be solved.

It is true, there would be a noticeable improvement in hand hygiene, however, I do not necessarily agree that the porosity of the artificial nail care product is a large factor in harboring pathogens. Is it a factor? It absolutely can be, but not the main one. I believe the problem lies in the fact there are far too many technicians who are doing a rushed and sloppy job with their work.

For instance, how many of you can look at your nails right now and see lifting, lumps, bumps, overrun product at the cuticle area and the side wall (sides of the nail) area? How many of you have infections or allergic reactions because of having certain artificial nail care products on your nails?

Although we can place a portion of the blame on the nail care product, the truth is, most of the blame, it seems, must go to:

1) The client who wears the artificial nail care product, who *does not* maintain the product on their nails in order to avoid lifting and who *does not* wash their hands appropriately.

2) The nail technician who does not follow proper sanitation guidelines and who *does not* take care and caution in the application of the product they are applying to their clients nails. When the nail plate is not appropriately cleansed and dehydrated and if the tools used are not appropriately disin-

fected, bacteria could be "*locked in*" under the artificial nail care product. This could lead to the breeding of bacteria which can cause infection.

I agree with the recommendation of the CDC. Nails, regardless of whether they are natural or artificial should be kept short. However, I also believe if the technicians did their job appropriately from start to finish and if the clients were directed by hospital management to maintain their artificial nails by making sure they were kept short in length and making sure there is no lifting, there would not be a problem with them having an artificial nail care product on their nails.

Unfortunately, as I have mentioned before, there is a gross shortage of quality nail technicians at this time and I am certain individuals in the medical industry do not always wash their hands as they have been instructed to.

And so, at the time of this entry, medical facilities across the country continue to revise their dress code policies.

Chapter 11

To Wax Or Not To Wax

Paraffin wax treatments for the hands and feet are a very popular service. They are soothing for those who have dry, chapped skin and can be therapeutic for those who have arthritis. Unfortunately, paraffin wax in the warmer can be the perfect place for bacteria to breed. How so?

Glad you asked. When I lived in Utah, I worked in Park City during the winter months. One year in particular, I worked at the Spa at the Canyon's Resort. In between clients one evening, I went to the front desk to ask the spa manager a question. As I got closer to the front desk, I heard a gentleman questioning the manager in regard to the chemical maintenance of the outside hot tub. He wanted to see the log book which would show him how often the chemicals in the hot tub were being monitored. The spa manager accommodated his request, which turned out to be a very good thing on her behalf, as he then informed her he was a physician and was at the resort for a medical convention. He also informed her he had a vested interest in the resort. He said the last time he was at the resort he acquired a rash shortly after getting out of the hot tub. He said he was able to trace the time of contact back to the hot tub and found the spa did not have the appropriate level of chemicals in it to render it acceptable for use by multiple people. Before the doctor left, I politely requested permission from him to ask a question. He kindly accepted my request.

I mentioned to him, I could not help but overhear what he had just said and was curious what his medical opinion was, on the paraffin wax units people use to dip their hands, feet and elbows in.

The doctor, a *cardiac surgeon* replied, *"That's simple, they are the perfect breeding ground for bacteria. The wax does not get hot enough to kill bacteria, if it did, you would not be able to dip your hands or feet in it without getting burned."*

Many in the nail care industry will argue that this is an untrue statement. They will respond saying *"there is no way anyone could become infected by dipping their hands, feet or elbows into the paraffin wax because as soon as you dip into the wax, the wax becomes hard so there would be no way that bacteria could be transmitted from one person to the next."* Consider the fact that the paraffin wax *does not* harden until after a person has removed their hands, feet or elbows from the wax, the first time. Therefore, bacteria *can* be transmitted from one person to the next via the first introduction into the paraffin wax.

The nail care industry has acknowledged this as an area of concern and has begun to experiment with different ways of achieving the benefits of paraffin wax treatments without having to dip. Ways such as dipping gauze strips into the wax and wrapping the gauze around the clients hands, feet or elbows. At least one manufacturer of the paraffin wax has added a "germ killer" to their wax stating it will kill all bacteria. My question is, what have they added to the paraffin wax and can it cause allergic reactions to the person who is dipping their hands feet, and elbows into it?

FYI

You should also be very cautious when you allow anyone to perform a hair removal service on you by way of waxing. Make sure the person who is going to perform the service is using a new spatula *every time* they dip into the wax. If they don't, they will be contaminating the wax with your germs and with the germs of all of those who went before you. The wax is warm and bacteria can thrive beautifully. Not a very comforting feeling is it?

Some individuals are very sensitive and will bleed a little when they are waxed. It does not take a rocket scientist to figure out how bad this situation could be and as if the information I have just enlightened you with was not enough, how would you feel if your technician double dipped a spatula into the same wax pot they used to give others before you, a Brazilian wax? Do you know what a Brazilian waxing consists of? A Brazilian wax, for those who do not know is, the complete removal of hair from the pubic, genital, buttock and rectal regions of the body.

Bottom line. If you are going to have any part of your body waxed, be sure the person who performs your waxing is not double dipping into the wax pot. Make sure they use a new spatula *every time* they go back into the wax. If the technician opens a new spatula in front of you, this is a good thing. If she/he continually uses the same spatula to dip into the wax and apply it to your body, this is a bad thing. Once again, make sure they use a new spatula *every time* they dip into the wax. If they don't, you could be the lucky recipient of a disgusting infection.

Chapter 12

What Is A MSDS?

Throughout this book, you may have noticed I have made reference to a MSDS (Material Data Safety Sheet) many times. For those who do not know what a MSDS is, it is a document that is used to provide important information to those using a manufacturers product/chemicals.

For instance, your nail technician is required to have a MSDS on *all* of the products they use in their place of business. The MSDS will give information in regard to the appropriate handling of a particular product/chemical as well as information on whether the product/chemical can or does pose health concerns in its usage.

You may be told *"there is no reason for you to have a copy of a MSDS."* I disagree! The MSDS will inform you of things such as what you may experience if you are overexposed to a particular product/

chemical. Central Nervous System Depression is one of the things that can happen, if you are sensitive or are overexposed to acrylic nail chemicals.

For those who use artificial nail care chemicals at home, it is very important you get a copy of the MSDS for the products you use so you can make sure you are not placing yourself or your family at risk of injury.

If you log onto ask.com and ask, "What is a MSDS?" you will be given numerous sites where you can go to learn more about the MSDS. One site in particular which I have found to be very good is **http://www. ilpi.com/MSDS/faq.**

Having a MSDS on the products you use, or are allowing a technician to use on you and knowing how to read them, could possibly keep you from serious injury.

Chapter 13

Manicure Nightmares

Have *you* ever gone into a salon or nail shop to get a manicure and walked out with your cuticles cut and bleeding? If so, you certainly are not alone.

I have heard of this happening more often than not. My question to you, is much the same as when someone has told me they were cut with the drill. "Are you certain, the tools the technician used on you, were appropriately cleaned and disinfected?"

Almost everyone has said they have no idea. If I were to ask *you,* what would *you* say? If I were to ask you if the technician used a *new* file on *your* nails, what would you say? Would *you* say, "I don't know?". Would you tell me the technician used the same file on you that was used on the client before you?

Unfortunately, this practice is all too common and *you* are the one to pay the price. As I have mentioned many times in this book, if a technician uses a tool on you that has not been appropriately cleaned and disinfected, and they cut you, you could contract one of many diseases or infections.

Keep in mind; disease and infection is a respecter of none. The *wealthy* are as much at risk of being injured as those who are considered *middle class* or *low income*. Take for instance, Paula Abdul. Ms. Abdul went public with information of how she contracted an infection in her thumb after receiving a manicure.

I tried to contact Ms. Abdul personally but was unsuccessful. However, I was able to reach her attorney who allowed me to ask a few questions and did confirm the infection Ms. Abdul had suffered from was indeed very serious, as the media had reported. Ms. Abdul was so upset about what had happened to her, she went to Sacramento in hopes of gaining the attention of California legislators, she wanted to implore stronger regulations in the area of sanitation and disinfection procedures within the nail care industry. What happened to Ms. Abdul is the same thing that has happened with many of you. She allegedly was worked on by a technician who did not appropriately clean and disinfect their manicuring tools. The technician punctured her skin in the process of giving her a manicure and she ended up with a serious infection. What happened to Ms. Abdul was worse than most, but not as bad as others.

About eight years ago a woman in Kansas City, Missouri had to have a portion of her index finger amputated because of a severe infection that had traveled into her bone. The infection was caused by a faulty nail care service.

You should be able to get a manicure without worrying you are going to be injured, infected, or worse, loose your finger.

You may want to consider taking your own manicuring tools with you and have your technician use your tools instead of theirs. If you decide to take your own tools, you need to make sure *you* appropriately cleanse and disinfect them before you put them away. If you do not, you can still run into problems. You can purchase all of the items individually or you purchase a kit of tools most often used for a manicure and pedicure procedure.

Keep in mind, taking your own tools

does not guarantee complete safety. If you are sitting at the table of a technician who does not follow appropriate guidelines for cleaning and disinfecting their work area, their environment, and their hands, you could still be the victim of a manicure nightmare. For example, if your technician cuts you and uses a dirty towel or a dirty paper towel to wipe the blood away, or if they use their finger to wipe the blood away, bacteria can contaminate the injured area and result in infection.

Bottom line, manicures can be a nice way of pampering yourself, but you have to become aware of your surroundings and make sure to protect yourself as much as you can from the hidden dangers of having them.

Chapter 14

Hepatitis C, From A Manicure?

Pretend you were not feeling well or maybe it was simply time for your annual check up. You go to your appointment, your doctor says things look good but he/she wants to run a few tests just to be sure. A few days later the receptionist at the doctor's office calls you saying the doctor wants to see you back in their office. Upon meeting with the doctor, you are told you have Hepatitis C. You are shocked because you have no idea how you could have contracted it. You have no tattoos. You are not an IV drug user. You do not have multiple sexual partners, and you have never had a blood transfusion. You are at a loss, wondering how this could possibly have happened to *you*.

For those of you who do not know what *Hepatitis C* is, it is a disease caused by a virus which causes inflammation of the liver that can lead to long term liver disease. In severe cases it can lead to death. Common symptoms can include; fever, headache, sore throat, nausea, aching joints and muscles, appetite loss, weakness, pain in the upper right quadrant of the abdomen and jaundice.

If this topic interests you, you can begin your journey to learn more about Hepatitis by logging onto **http://epidemic.org.**

According to numerous medical industry professionals, including C. Everett Koop, who is the former United States Surgeon General and an organization known as The National Kidney Foundation, Hepatitis C can be spread in one of many ways. It can be spread by a tattoo and body piercing artist who does not appropriately sterilize their needles, and by IV drug users who share needles. It can be spread by an infected individual who has multiple sexual partners and by sharing items such as a razor, tooth brush and manicuring tools with a person who is infected with the virus.

The technician who does not appropriately clean and disinfect their manicuring tools after every client is placing you at risk. If the technician cuts a client who has Hepatitis C and then works on you with the same tools without cleaning and disinfecting the tools first, you could become infected if they cut you.

FYI

Not only should you be concerned with contracting Hepatitis C, you may want to become familiar with *Hepatitis B* also. *Hepatitis B* is contracted much the same way as Hepatitis C. It can cause cirrhosis and liver cancer and is said to be one hundred times more contagious than HIV. It can be contracted if, for example, you have a cut, scratch or scrape and you come in contact with a contaminated surface, object, or if you touch the contaminated surface or object then rub your eyes or mouth.

Chapter 15

Allergic Reactions

Allergic reaction to artificial nail care products is one of the most common problems experienced by the client of a nail technician. Most often allergic reaction occurs because the individual has been overexposed to the product/chemical which is being used during their nail care service.

For instance, let's say you have been going to salon "X" for ten years. You have never had a problem until the last time you had your nails done at which time your cuticle area and the surrounding tissue (skin) started to burn, itch, throb, hurt, turn red, blister, swell, crack and/or bleed. Some of you have experienced only one of these symptoms, some of you have experienced all of them. Some of you have been in so much pain you could do nothing but cry and when you called your technician to tell them what was happening you were told it was "no big deal", then you were directed to soak your nails in alcohol and take an anti-histamine to minimize the itching.

If the product you have on your nails is an acrylic nail product, you were most likely reacting to the liquid monomer. If the person who has been doing your nails has been touching any part of your skin with the brush they use to mix the acrylic liquid monomer and the acrylic powder, they have been overexposing you to the liquid monomer. In order to *not* overexpose you to the chemicals which are being used to create your acrylic nails, the technician must use the correct brush as well as the correct liquid monomer to powder ratio. If a technician uses a large brush, *which many do in order to get your nails done quickly*, it is almost certain they will saturate your skin with excess liquid monomer.

This is one of the areas where the problem starts. Reason being, the liquid monomer is an active chemical and it is looking for something to bond with. When it is mixed with the powder, the bonding of the two take place, thus your acrylic nails. If there is more liquid monomer than powder, the excess liquid monomer will penetrate your skin.

Allergic reactions can be an indication that your body's immune system has detected an intruder. When this happens, your body's defense mechanism will kick in and begin to fight the intruder. This is where the blisters and swelling come from. Keep in mind, once you have an allergic reaction to acrylic nail products, you will always have a reaction to them. As a matter of fact, some of you have had such a severe reaction to acrylics you can not tolerate having dental work done on your teeth or your bridge work because the chemical structure between the acrylic products and the dental compounds are much the same.

Such an incident happened to my friend Debbie. I met Debbie *after* she had gotten her nails done at a nail shop, which we later found, was using Methyl Methacrylate liquid. Shortly after having her nails done, Debbie called me. She said she was in pain and her fingers itched horribly. We scheduled an appointment to remove her acrylic nails.

Months later, Debbie needed to have dental work done. After she had the work done, she called me and told me that blisters were beginning to form on the inside of her mouth. She also said it was very painful.

She asked me if it could be because she was allergic to acrylic nail products. I told her it was possible. Debbie went to her doctor and found out that indeed, she was having an allergic reaction to the dental work which was triggered by the reaction she had experienced previously from the acrylic nail product.

FYI
Additional symptoms of allergic reactions can be, but are not limited to:

- Itchy, watery eyes
- Loss of smell
- Loss of taste
- Lifting of the natural nail at the free edge
- Loss of the entire natural nail plate
- A rash on other areas of the body

If you have had an allergic reaction to acrylic nail products, it would be wise on your part to stop having the product used on you. As I mentioned before, once you react you will always react. The allergic reaction may be minimal at first, but over time, you could even wind up having an allergic reaction such as the one my friend Debbie had or one much worse.

If you have not had an allergic reaction and would like to try to avoid one, *DO NOT* allow a technician to use a *large* brush to create your acrylic nails. It is virtually impossible to keep the brush off of your skin, thus impossible to keep excess liquid monomer from penetrating through your skin.

You should also be careful of the technician who uses a small brush. Many technicians will use a small brush to dip the tip of the brush into the liquid monomer and then "clean up" the smile line of a white tip acrylic nail. They do this because it allows the brush to smooth out the white acrylic in order to get a sharp, crisp looking smile line. The end result is usually very pretty, but remember, excess liquid monomer will find, a place to go and that place is, *absorbed through your skin.*

Chapter 16

Mold And Fungus

There is such a misconception about what mold and fungus is, and I am quite surprised at the number of technicians who are giving you the incorrect information. Simply explained, you have been told the "green" stuff you may have seen on your nails is either "mold" or "fungus". The truth is the "green" stuff is actually the byproduct of bacteria

This type of bacteria is called pseudomonas. The byproduct is typically green in color but can begin to turn black. Pseudomonas bacterial infection can happen between the natural nail plate and nail bed as well as between an artificial nail product and the nail plate.

When occurring between the natural nail and an artificial nail product, the cause can be one of several things. If it is detected between the natural nail and an artificial product but there is absolutely no lifting of the product, the bacteria may have been "locked" in under the product due to inappropriate cleansing and dehydration of the natural nail plate *before* the artificial nail product was applied.

If there are areas where the product has lifted, water and moisture can penetrate through and create the perfect breeding ground for the pseudomonas bacteria. Thus the "greenies."

If this happens to you, have your technician remove the artificial nail product immediately. Removing the product will allow the affected areas to dehydrate. The technician should also disinfect the area. This can be done in a number of ways, one way is to soak the infected area in 91-99 percent alcohol for a couple of minutes. Upon removal of the old product and disinfecting the natural nail, you may (should you chose) have product re-applied. The bacteria will be gone but the green color will have to grow out because it is stained onto the natural nail plate.

FUNGUS

A fungal infection is usually characterized by white or yellowish, crusty build-up under the natural nail plate.

Fungal infection is more common in the toe nails than it is in the fingernails. To be determined a "fungal" infection a sample must be taken by a physician and cultured. A nail technician's scope of abilities is to help make the client's hands and feet look more attractive. They should **NEVER** *diagnose* you with a fungal infection, as they are not qualified to do so. Once again, you should seek the advice and attention of your physician, dermatologist or podiatrist. Furthermore, if you know you have a fungal infection you should not allow the technician to work on you until it is gone.

Chapter 17

Pedicure Nightmares

As I begin to write this chapter, I have mountains of research on this topic and it is disheartening to know so many innocent people have been hurt. Something which should have been pleasant, relaxing and beautifying turned into a nightmare for a significant number of individuals and their families.

There are isolated incidents before 2000, but beginning late in 2000, all hell broke loose in Watsonville, California. The media began releasing reports in regard to individuals who had contracted infections after receiving pedicures at a local nail shop. The bacterial infection was mycobacterium fortuitum, which is a bacterium in the family of tuberculosis.

The victims of a nail shop suffered from purple pus filled lesions and boils on their legs. Reports began to surface September 30, 2000 with a dozen clients of a Watsonville, California nail shop complaining of "strange skin irritations" on their legs. By October 26, 2000, the Health Department stated nearly 140 clients had reported "sores" on their legs after having a pedicure.

Many of the victims had to be on antibiotics for six months or more. One of the victims was a young girl when she contracted the infection. As if the infection the victims were suffering from was not enough, they were also told the antibiotic treatment they would need to take in order to kill the infection, could significantly weaken their immune system.

FYI

If your immune system is weakened it is possible, you may become prime target for a number of additional illness, infection and/or disease.

When the "powers that be" investigated the ordeal, they found "black, tarry slime" in the jets of the pedicure unit. The Watsonville, California nail shop was not the only one investigated. Nail shops around the country were also investigated and were found guilty of the same filth. The Watsonville ordeal generated a multi-million dollar recovery for the victims who where injured and the two most recent cases were settled in early 2005.

After all was said and done and the cause was found, it came down to lack of sanitation and disinfection of the whirlpool spa chairs. Try to imagine this. Over two hundred pedicures per week could have been performed in that shop and if the whirlpool spas were NEVER cleaned and NEVER disinfected, all of the shavings, scrapings, dead skin cells and blood (possible if you were cut) from your feet would have been commingling with that of hundreds before you.

It has been many years since the Watsonville ordeal. The pedicure nightmares are far from over though. In 2006, two women died, as a result of infections they contracted after receiving a pedicure.

One woman was from Texas. She was cut during her pedicure and contracted an infection called MRSA (Methicillin Resistant Staphylococcus Aureus) which became very aggressive. Her blood became infected which caused a fatal heart attack in February 2006. She was only 46 years old. The other woman was from California and was

43 when she died in early August 2006. She died from a mycobacterial infection in her leg. An infection she acquired after receiving a pedicure at nail shop. Information on this incident can also be found by logging onto **http://www.bohnlaw.com/case11.jsp.**

I encourage you to take a look at this site. Something else you may want to be aware of is fungal infection. This type of infection tends to go untreated by the individual because, although unsightly in the beginning stages, it is usually painless. However, if the infection goes untreated long enough, it could worsen to the point of requiring removal of the toe nail, or worse, the entire toe. This is possible, if, the infection travels to the bone.

A fungal infection can be systemic, which may be visible as growing from the cuticle area toward the free edge (end) of the nail plate or it could be topical which may be visible as growing from the free edge (end) of the nail plate going toward the cuticle area. A fungal infection will not go away on its own. It can be treated a number of ways depending upon the severity. One of the most aggressive treatments is an oral medication. Unfortunately, if you choose to take this medication, you now have to be concerned with potential liver damage because the type of medication used to kill fungal infection can cause liver damage.

As I have mentioned in other chapters, you do not have to stop having pedicure services done, you do however, need to educate yourself which will help you to make informed decisions and choices in regard to your health, safety and well being. To begin this process, read Chapter 20, *"Clean It Up"*. This chapter will assist you in becoming aware of how pedicure units should be cleaned and disinfected.

On a final note, the incidents noted in this chapter, all resulted from clients having pedicure services performed on them by technicians who incorporate the use of a whirlpool spa unit during the pedicure service. *Do not* make the mistake though, of thinking you are safe because you *never* have your pedicures done in a whirlpool spa unit. No matter what type of unit your technician uses to place your feet in, you are at risk of infection if they do not clean and disinfect the whirlpool, basin, bowl or sink correctly.

Chapter 18

California, Cosmetics And The Law

What does one have to do with the other? I will gladly tell you. I would first like to say, this chapter will only be of interest to you if you are concerned with knowing about the chemicals the cosmetic companies utilize to manufacture the products you purchase and use. Products such as nail polish, artificial nail products, make-up, lotions, shampoos, powders, hair spray, hair dye, the list goes on and on.

The beginning of this research takes me back to September 9, 2003. I attended a women's conference earlier in the day where Erin Brockovich was the lunch hour keynote speaker. As Ms. Brockovich finished her presentation, nearly all of the attendee's moved on to their next session which made it fairly simple for me to get her attention long enough to ask her if she would give me two minutes of her time. She was busy signing autographs, but took a second to look up and ask me what it was about. I said *"Children and toxic chemicals."* Ms. Brockovich stopped what she was doing and asked me if she could call me on her way back home. I said yes and gave her my number.

Ms. Brockovich did not call as she said she would, which worked out for the best because destiny then took over. It was nearing 7:00 p.m. when I had resolved to the fact she was not going to call, so I logged onto my computer and began to randomly search specific topics to see what I could find. It was not too long before I came across a statement Senator Edward Kennedy had written in regard to his position on a FDA reform bill. The statement was released on September 10, 1997. The passing of this bill would have made the cosmetic industry exempt from state regulation. Translated, manufacturers of cosmetics (all inclusive) would not have had to disclose to the public whether or not they were using chemicals that could harm the consumer nor would they have to place cautionary, statements on labels of products that could be harmful, in any way.

By the information given in the report, Senator Kennedy seemed to be completely against this and believed not only did the public have the right to know what was in the products they were consuming, but to also be cautioned if the product had the ability to be hazardous to their health, safety and well being. Remember, the report was written in September of 1997. I found it in September of 2003. Exactly six years had passed since it had been written. I called the phone number of the contact person named on the document, I wanted to know if Senator Kennedy still held his position in regard to this issue. The answer I received was, "Yes, the Senator still holds his position on this issue." The fire of interest and curiosity had instantly been turned up and my desire to search for more information on this topic grew deeper.

In 2004, I found information on Assembly Bill 2012 which was sponsored by California Assemblywoman Judy Chu. The bills topic was *Cosmetics: Cancer and Reproductive Toxicity.* Seems as though Assemblywoman Chu holds the same position as Senator Kennedy, believing the public has the right to know what is in the cosmetic products they are using. Especially if some of the chemicals are known cancer causing agents or reproductive toxins. Unfortunately, A.B. 2012 was killed. In other words, it did not pass.

It may have been the end of A.B. 2012 however on October 7, 2005, Senate Bill 484, *Cosmetics: Chronic Health Effects*, authored by California Senator, Carol Migden, co-authored by California Senators, Alquist, Kuehl, Ortiz, and Torlakson and California Assembly members Berg, Chan, Evans, Goldberg, Karnette, Lieber, Montanez and Nation made it. On October 7, 2005, California Governor, Arnold Schwarzenegger, signed Senate Bill 484, it was filed with the Secretary of State on the same day. California law now requires manufacturers of cosmetics to disclose to the public, cancer causing agents and reproductive toxins they may be utilizing to manufacture their products.

Personally, I am thrilled the bill passed. I encourage you to take a look at it. The information you find will help assist you in being able to make more informed decisions in regard to the products you use and the products you will allow to be used on you.

For detailed information on Senate Bill 484, Chapter 729, *Cosmetics: Chronic Health Effects*, further known and cited as the *California Safe Cosmetics Act of 2005*, you can log onto **http://leginfo. ca.gov**, click on *Bill Information*, choose the *2005-2006 Session*, check *bill number* and *search SB-484*. Click on *SB-484-Midgen*, Cosmetics: chronic health effects. Click on *chaptered PDF*.

The passing of this bill may possibly be the catalyst for change throughout the United States of America and quite possibly the world. Sadly, though, only those manufacturers who have annual aggregate sales of cosmetic products over a million dollars within, and outside of the state of California, have to comply with this new law. Personally, I believe *all* manufacturers should have to comply. Unfortunately, this is not the case. At the very least, I think we can say this is a good start and push in the right direction. The direction of a much needed change!

The Solution

Ok, so now it is time to find out what you can do to ensure you do not become the victim of a careless nail technician. If you have read the chapters prior to this one, you have without question, become very aware of several major problems within the nail care industry. The real solution to all of these problems is very simple. Take control of your own health, safety and well being. As I have said before, no one is going to take care of you, as well as you will yourself. The following chapters will assist you in being able to make sound and informed decisions on who you will allow to perform manicures, pedicures and artificial nail care services on you.

Chapter 19

Choosing A Technician

The information you have been given
and empowered with should make the days
of you walking blindly into a potentially
hazardous situation near non-existent.

No longer will a technician who is doing your nails be able to cut corners and
put you at risk without you knowing it.
Following are several tips on how you may
begin your search for a reputable, qualified technician.

First! When you walk into the business, do you feel comfortable? Does it look
clean? Are the tables clean? Is there an
overbearing chemical smell? Are the technicians wearing masks?

If you do not feel comfortable, do not
be afraid to turn around and leave. Keep
looking for the right place for you. If, on the

other hand, you are comfortable, go ahead and stay. Just remember to ask questions BEFORE you allow anyone to work on you.

Second! Ask the technician who will be performing your service if they have a valid license to be performing nail care services. If they say yes, ask to see it. If the license does not have their picture on it, ask them to show you a second form of identification with their name and picture on it, to validate the nail technician license they have shown you is indeed theirs and not someone else's. If they refuse to accommodate your request, you should NOT allow them to work on you! Reason being, it is not unusual to find several manicurists working under one manicurists license. Illegal ? Yes. Still it is done throughout the United States on a daily basis.

Third, and most important! Ask the technician to explain how they disinfect their manicure and pedicure tools, their work stations, and their pedicure bowls, chairs, basins and if they clean and disinfect after **every** client. (See the next chapter, *"Clean It Up"* for California's *recommendations* on disinfecting pedicure stations. (Our *recommendations* may be the *regulations* of all states very soon.) If the person you are talking with fails to answer the questions you have asked, to your understanding and your satisfaction, you may want to consider leaving.

Fourth! If you are satisfied with the answers you have been given, *before* you allow the technician to perform any service on you, ask them what type of products they will be using on you. For example, if you are going to have acrylic nails done, ask the technician what type of acrylic product they use (refer to Chapter 5 for information on the different types of nail care products which are available to you.)

Be aware of the technician who uses a cloth towel on their table with a paper towel on the top of it. The reason you need to be aware of this is because many technicians will often use the same towel all day long, maybe even for days at a time, simply shaking it off in between clients. What the technician will usually do is, place a new paper towel on top of the dirty towel they have used with the clients before you and are now using during your service.

This obviously, is NOT sanitary and should NOT be done. The technicians table should be cleaned and disinfected after every client and a clean towel should be provided for *every* client. *PERIOD!*

Look for a technician who regularly attends ongoing education and training classes. Look for valid certificates of completion for this training. Look for someone who will patiently and willingly address all of your questions and concerns *before* you place your life into their hands.

Having said this, well trained nail technicians are few and far between, but, they do exist and they are worth looking for.

Chapter 20

Clean It Up

The information you find in this chapter, can assist in you gaining a solid understanding of what to look for when you initially walk into a salon, spa or nail shop. It can also help you to understand how your technician should be cleaning and disinfecting their work station, equipment and tools.

Let's start with you walking into the establishment. As I have mentioned in previous chapters, take a look around. Is the business clean? Is the floor clean? Is the technician's tables clean? If the trash cans are overflowing with trash, if the tables are a mess, you may want to consider taking your business elsewhere. The things I have just mentioned may be possible indicators that you are in a bacteria infested environment. If the technician cannot take the time to clean the simplest areas, chances are, they are NOT following appropriate sanitation and disinfection procedures for their equipment either.

The technicians table should be clean and free of dust and debris from the prior client. If the technician uses a towel on top of the table it must be a clean towel, not one they have used with prior clients. There should be no food or drink at the table unless the drink is in a cup with a lid.

BEFORE your technician touches your hands both of you *must* have either, washed your hands with soap and water and/or used a hand sanitizer to rid your hands of as many germs as possible.

Your technician should then inspect your nails (and hands) looking for any adverse conditions such as allergic reactions, cuts, scrapes, or skin disease. It would not be a bad idea for you to take a visual of your technician's hands as well.

FYI

Ruth Werner, author of *"A Massage Therapists Guide to Pathology"* says, *"It would be a good idea to follow universal precaution."* This means, assume everyone has the potential to infect you with one disease or another and make sure you take all steps to avoid being infected.

Before you allow the technician to begin the service, you should first decide whether you are going to allow them to use *their* tools on you or have them use the ones you may have brought with you. Every form of the media has covered the problems in regard to the nail care industry. At the end of their story, the reporter always suggests you take your own tools to your nail care appointment. The reason for this is, it seems like an obvious fix for a very real problem. It would not be a bad idea to do this, but you may want to consider the following: If you cannot trust your technician to clean and disinfect *their* tools appropriately, do you really want to allow them to work on you at all?

For those of you, who have a service performed on you requiring the use of a drill; make sure the drill bits are clean and disinfected. Look at the bit and make sure there is no debris or dust particles embedded in it. Ask the technician if they have cleaned and disinfected it. If the technician is going to use a sander band, make sure it is a brand new one. Sander bands are a one time use item that must be thrown away after each client. As for nail files, some can be cleaned and disinfected and some can not.

Nail files are generally very inexpensive so you wouldn't be out of line to ask your technician to use a brand new nail file on you every time you have your nails done. You may want to check your states guidelines on the use of nail files. Some states say it is ok for a technician to clean and disinfect their nail files, then use them on a different client. Some states forbid this.

If you have taken a good look around the establishment and have asked questions and you feel comfortable with everything, including the type of product the technician is going to use on you and their application technique, by all means, stay and allow the technician to begin the service you have been scheduled for. If you are not completely comfortable, you should leave. Continue to look for a place and a technician you can trust and be comfortable with.

The information I just shared with you was mainly directed towards what you may want to look for when you initially walk into an establishment to have a nail care or beauty service performed on you and what should happen *before* the technician starts to perform a nail care service on you.

If you are going to have a pedicure performed on you, you will need to decide whether or not you want to put your feet and legs in a whirlpool spa or not. After reading *"Pedicure Nightmares"* you know what could possibly happen to you.

This situation has gotten so bad and so out of hand that *California's Department of Consumer Affairs* has recently released *recommendations* on how all pedicure units should be cleaned and disinfected. As a matter of fact, *Gary Duke, Legal Counsel to the California Board of Barbering and Cosmetology* says the state of California has begun to take emergency steps not only to release updated *recommendations* on how pedicure units should be cleaned and disinfected, but will soon release *regulations* of how it should be done. The difference between a *recommendation* and a *regulation* would be; if the technician does not follow the *recommended* cleaning and disinfection procedure, they *may* be cited and fined. If they do not follow the *regulations* for the cleaning and disinfection procedure, they may find themselves and/or their business cited and fined with a larger penalty and in far worse trouble.

A full document on what California technicians have recently received can be found by logging onto **http://www. barbercosmo.ca.gov/** then clicking on *Whirlpool Footspa Safety*. For those who may not have access to a computer at home or at work, but want to know what the *recommended* procedure is, here in California, consider going to your local library, you can use one of their computers or you can ask a friend or family member if they would go to the website and print the document for you.

The truth is, California leads the way in many areas. I believe the nail care industry is going to experience change worldwide, as a direct result of the changes we are currently making here in the state of California. Changes which are certain to raise the standards in the nail care industry.

Texas though, leads the way in a very important area. This state will soon require that all non porus manicure and pedicure tools be *sterilized*. Currently California requires *disinfection* of these items. Speaking of manicure and pedicure tools and disinfection, if your technician uses tools or items on you that are porous, you should know, the items must be thrown away after they are finished using them on you. A few examples of porous items are, orangewood sticks (wooden cuticle pusher), emery boards, certain nail files, buffer blocks, pumice stones or blocks and sponge toe separators.

Non-porous manicure and pedicure tools can be re-used AFTER they have been appropriately cleaned and disinfected. Several examples of non-porous manicure and pedicure tools are; metal or plastic cuticle pushers, metal cuticle nippers, fingernail trimmers, toe nail trimmers, certain pedicure foot files, nail brushes and metal pedicure tools.

You now know that all *porous* items used for performing a manicure, pedicure or artificial nail care service must be thrown away after they have been used on you. What most of you do not know is how the *non-porous* items should be disinfected.

As I mentioned earlier, the state of Texas will soon require *non-porous* manicure and pedicure tools be *sterilized* by means of an autoclave. An autoclave is what hospitals, medical facilities, dentists and tattoo artists use to sterilize their non-porous equipment.

An autoclave sterilizes non-porous equipment by means of steam and very high temperatures completely destroying all bacteria and spores. Appropriate guidelines must be followed according to manufacturer's guidelines. If the guidelines are not followed, the tools and equipment should be considered contaminated. There are many different autoclaves a technician can choose from. To find out more on how an autoclave works you can do a search on **ask.com**.

As for appropriate disinfection procedures, this would consist of scrubbing the non-porous tools with an antibacterial soap and warm water. Using an antibacterial soap and a scrub brush will help to loosen the bacteria and debris on the tools, which should then be rinsed well and submerged in an Environmental Protection Agency (EPA) registered liquid hospital disinfectant that claims it is a bactericide, virucide and fungicide, for 10 minutes (or as directed by the product manufacturer).Upon completion of the time in the disinfectant, the tools should then be removed from the solution, rinsed well, dried and placed in a dust free container labeled *disinfected.*

FYI

If you have a certain level of comfort because you have watched your technician place their tools in the container that has *blue* liquid in it immediately after they have finished with the client before you, don't feel so comfortable.

As I mentioned a little bit ago, the tools must be washed and rinsed *BEFORE* they are placed in the disinfection solution. If the tools are placed in the disinfection solution without being washed and rinsed first, *consider the tools contaminated and do not allow the technician to use them on you.*

Something else you should be aware of is; nail technicians have been known to use *blue* window cleaner in their disinfection container instead of a disinfection solution. Why? Simply explained, it is far less expensive than purchasing the disinfection solution they are supposed to be using. The technicians who do this are seriously cutting corners and have assumed you would never become aware of what they are doing. They know, many of you look for the "blue stuff" in the jar and when you see the "blue stuff" in the jar, you most likely will not question them on whether or not they disinfect their tools because, it seems as though they are doing it right there in front of you. Sad, but true and now that you have been made aware of this issue, you may want to consider asking your technician if you could see the disinfectant they use

Going back to the appropriate disinfecting product, in order for the solution to work correctly, it must be mixed according to the manufacturers directions and it should be changed according to how busy the technician is.

If the solution has become cloudy when normally it is a clear blue, it is contaminated and old. Consider the tools that have come out of that particular solution contaminated. Furthermore, if the tools are not **completely** submerged in the appropriate disinfection solution (after being washed and rinsed) consider the tools contaminated. Tools that are partially submerged, even though the disinfection solution has been changed, are only partially disinfected. The container used to hold the solution can be one that is made for professional nail technicians and hair stylists or it can be any other sort of container. No matter what is used, the tools must be completely covered by the disinfection solution.

Last but not least, in regard to cleaning and disinfecting manicure and pedicure tools, is the nail brush. I have yet to meet one of you who will say with confidence, your technician hands you a cleaned and disinfected nail brush when they ask you to go wash your hands after they are done doing your nails.

I constantly hear that you are asked to go wash your hands, using the nail brush which is sitting by the sink. Who knows how long it has been there or how many have used it before you. If your technician wants you to go and wash your hands for any reason, and they want you to use a nail brush, make sure they give you one that is clean and disinfected.

At this point we have covered a number of the things you should be aware of and should be looking for when you walk into a salon, spa or nail shop. We have also covered the basic procedure for cleaning and disinfecting manicure and pedicure tools. It is now time to go over a few points which can help you become aware of whether or not you are about to place your feet and legs into a dirty pedicure basin.

As I mentioned earlier in this chapter, technicians here in California have recently received updated *recommendations* on how pedicure units (all inclusive) should be cleaned and disinfected. This information, once again, can be found in detail by logging onto **http://www.barbercosmo.ca.gov/** then clicking on *Whirlpool Footspa Safety*.

The basic *recommendation* is; the pedicure unit (all inclusive) must be drained of all water, the unit should be rinsed, all residue should then be scrubbed off of the walls and surrounding areas of the basin and rinsed again. The unit should then be filled with water, adding to it the correct amount of an Environmental Protection Agency (EPA) registered hospital liquid disinfectant and circulated (if applicable) for 10 minutes or per manufacturers directions. The unit must then be drained, rinsed well and wiped dry with a clean paper towel (not a towel). Again, these are the very basic *recommendations* for cleaning and disinfecting a pedicure unit. There are more in-depth *recommendations* for the whirlpool spa which would be worth becoming familiar with.

For those who will continue to have pedicures, you may want to know, you should not shave your legs for twenty four hours *prior* to receiving the pedicure service. When you shave your legs, quite often you acquire micro tears and tiny nicks. You may, or may not, be aware of their presence but injuries, even as small as these, can be dangerous. They can be prime ports of entry for bacteria which may be lingering in the pedicure unit.

If a pedicure unit is not appropriately cleaned and disinfected and if you have cuts on your skin and you receive a pedicure in the dirty pedicure unit, this, as you already know, could lead to you becoming the next *"Pedicure Nightmare"*

Bear with me, we are almost finished.

If your technician has been storing your tools for you, either in a box or maybe in a zip top type of plastic bag, stop allowing them to do this. Storing tools in a zip top type of plastic bag creates the perfect breeding ground for bacteria and is actually against some states rules and regulations. Same goes with storing the tools in a box. Check *your* states rules and regulations on this one.

Finally, does your technician use a *"credo"* blade on your feet when they give you a pedicure? A *"credo"* blade is a razor type of instrument which many technicians use during a pedicure procedure to remove stubborn, thick callus areas on the feet. They are a very sharp and potentially dangerous tool, prohibited in some states, illegal in others.

Do you know what *your* states rules and regulations say about this?

Chapter 21

Why This? Why Now?

It was October 25, 1997. My family and I had just moved to our new home in Sandy, Utah. Somewhere between leaving Fresno, California and arriving in Utah, I had broken a nail. It was really no big deal because I knew exactly where all of my nail supplies were packed. I knew I could fix the broken nail over the weekend. However, as we drove through our new neighborhood, a nail salon caught my attention. Upon seeing this salon, I quickly decided I was going to treat myself and have someone else do my nails rather than do them myself. Shortly after we arrived at our new home, I called the salon and made an appointment for the next day. When I arrived for my appointment, I noticed the salon looked nice and seemed clean. I was not uncomfortable being there. However, as I sat down at the nail technician's table I became a little apprehensive. The technician seemed to be very nice, however, her work area left a lot to be desired. It was apparent she had not cleaned her tabletop after her previous client. There were brushes, files, and implements in a cup. The table was dusty and it was obvious the files had been used on prior clients. None the less, I decided to stay. Though I was not impressed with the situation at hand, I was looking forward to having my nails done by someone else for a change. Before the nail technician began the service, I did ask her to clean her table, her implements, and use a new file on my nails. She was kind enough to accommodate my request. As she began to work, we began a conversation. This very conversation would be the one that would change my life and launch my career as a nail care educator.

I received my California Cosmetology license in 1983. An individual holding this type of license is legally entitled to perform services in hair care, skin care, and nail care. My area of expertise had always been hairstyling. Nail care held second place with me until my conversation with the nail technician. I had planned on applying for a Utah cosmetology license however, things quickly changed. I asked the nail technician how long she had been doing nails. She said for several years. I then asked her where she went to school. The young lady told me she was privately taught. My first thought was, *"My goodness, we must be living in a wealthy area."* My second thought was, *"How can this be? I thought everyone had to go to beauty school or nail technology school to learn how to do nails."* So I said, *"Privately taught, it must have been wonderful, to have one-on-one training. Was the course expensive?"* Her reply was, *"Oh, it was only one hundred and fifty dollars."* I was shocked because nail care courses cost about two thousand dollars. My next question to her was, *"How long was the course?"* She replied, *"It was only a one-day course because you don't have to have a license to do nails in Utah."*

At that point, we were halfway into the service and I was absolutely blown away by what I had just heard. I gently pulled my hands away from the nail technician. She was surprised, and asked me what was wrong. I told her that I had just moved to Utah from California and I was a licensed cosmetologist. After several minutes of discussion, I asked her if she would be offended if I helped her with her technique and with the process of doing a fill. I was glad to see she was the type of person who wanted to learn, and was curious and open to what I had just proposed. I began to share information with her on how she should clean her table after each client and explained to her how to apply the acrylic in order to avoid over exposure to the acrylic nail chemicals. (At *that point in time I was still using acrylic nail products.*)

When it was time for me to go, she thanked me for helping her. She said she had never been taught anything more than how to dip the brush into the liquid and then into the powder and apply it to the nail. When I got home, I told my husband what had just happened and even though doing nails was not my first choice of areas in which to build a career, I could not let an opportunity to go to work *immediately* just pass by. So, after we settled into our house, I chose a day to visit a few a salons.

I chose to work at a salon which was very nice and close to my home. It didn't take me very long to build a strong client base and shortly after I had started at the salon one of my clients asked me if I would teach her daughter how to do nails. At that time I had no desire to show anyone how to do nails. My first response was, "I'm not a teacher and I wouldn't know where to begin." My client was very persistent and asked me if I would *"please"* think about it. At first thought, teaching someone how to do what I was doing made me a little nervous. I had no idea where to begin. I did think about it however, and the next time I saw my client I told her yes, I would teach her daughter. I found out what the guidelines were in order to do this in the state of Utah. Several months and a lot of activity in my life had passed before the opportunity to open my salon and nail academy presented itself, which then lead me to an even deeper involvement within nail care industry and later, to the introduction of an alternative artificial nail care product. When I first opened my nail school, I used acrylic nail care products. Not too long after I had opened, I quit using acrylics and started using and teaching an alternative artificial nail care product, my school then became the *first* Nail Technology School in the state specializing in training nail technicians to *master manicures, pedicures, and* the application of a *safer artificial nail care product.*

Shortly after opening my academy, I had my first of several interviews with the television, radio, and newspaper media regarding sanitation and chemical awareness issues in the nail care industry. I also became a member of the National Cosmetology Association (NCA) SLC, Utah Affiliate #4 and was on the Board of Directors and Educational Committee for this affiliate. I, along with many others played a significant role in Utah passing into law mandatory licensing of nail technicians. Prior to the passing of this bill, Utah had not had *mandatory* licensing for nail technicians for over two decades.

Many meetings happened prior to the passing of the mandatory licensing bill. One, in particular, was a huge factor in why I decided to write this book.

I received a call from Mr. Clyde Ormond, Utah's Department of Professional Licensing Bureau Manager, asking me to attend a meeting in regard to the licensing issue. Mr. Ormond told me all attendees would be allowed five minutes to speak on the reasons they believed the mandatory licensing bill should pass. I accepted Mr. Ormond's invitation to speak at this meeting, planning to speak on the importance of chemical awareness. When the day came to attend the meeting, I was there, along with about ten other individuals who were representing the nail care and skin care industry. When my turn came, I indeed did speak on the importance of chemical awareness. I chose to discuss an incident in which a nail technician had caught fire from placing acetone in a microwave to warm it up. (Chapter 2 *"Acetone Explosion."*) When I finished, another nail care educator, who has since passed away but was very well known in the state of Utah, stood up to speak. This woman's comment was, *"I think what happened to that person is very sad, but let's face it, accidents happen."* I could not believe what I had just heard! While it is true accidents do happen, I was appalled that what happened to Debbie Greenwood was being responded to in such a cold and uncaring manner.

It was then that I decided I would write a book in regard to the nail care industry in order to increase public awareness. There are so many more details of how *this* book came to be. Suffice it to say, everything has worked together in arriving at *this* point.

What you have read, is what *"CAN"* happen to you as you receive manicures, pedicures, or artificial nail care services and most importantly, it was written to help *you,* the consumer, in order to help you make more informed decisions in regard to your health, safety, and well being, *BEFORE,* you have one of these services performed on you.

Afterword

Upon conclusion, my greatest hope is that this book has been of help to you in some way. You may have noticed it was written in a way that would give you a foundational understanding of what is happening in the nail care industry, along with information on how and where you can gain further knowledge in this area. I have written this way because I believe, as I have heard many times;

"If you give a person a fish... you feed them for a day,... if you teach a person to fish,... you feed them for a lifetime."

It has been my experience, one will gain and retain more subject matter if they are provided with a strong foundation as well as given information they can use to continue to build upon.

Respectfully,

Lisa Ann Bowles

REFERENCES

Here you will find a list of product manufacturers and suppliers as well as a number of website addresses which can help you further your knowledge base regarding the nail care industry. Although I am not in favor of acrylic nails, I have included two of the most reputable manufacturers of acrylic nail products worldwide. I have done this because, I know many of you will continue to have acrylic nail products applied to your nails, and I want you to be as safe as possible while you do it. The companies I have listed are well known for having some of the best training programs available for the technicians who use their products. They will also help you locate a technician who has been qualified in the use of their product. I have chosen to list these companies in particular because, in my opinion, they possess a high level of professionalism and integrity which is the same reason I have listed the other companies.

Awareness Information

http://www.mpausa.org
The Methacrylate Producers Association. Information on Methyl Methacrylate and Ethyl Methacrylate liquid monomer.

http://www.ilpi.com/MSDS/faq
Better understand what to look for and how to read a Material Safety Date Sheet.

http://epidemic.org
A great site for learning more about hepatitis.

http://www.nictesting.org
Links to all of the State Boards of Cosmetology across the United State which will allow you to gain information on what your states rules and regulations are for the area of nail technology.

http://www.barbercosmo.ca.gov
The direct address for the California Board of Barbering and Cosmetology where you will find the update recommendations for cleaning and disinfecting pedicure units (all inclusive).

http://www.ask.com
This site is GREAT! You can go here and ask

any question you want and get links to websites from around the world that will help you find your answers.

http://www.bohnlaw.com/case11.jsp
The website of a law firm which has handled a number of lawsuits for victims of pedicure infections. A great source of information.

http://www.fda.gov
This address will allow you to find the report "Artificial Nail Remover Poses Poisoning Risk". You will need to search "Cyanide Death" then click on FDA/CFSAN Cosmetics: Update on Artificial Nail Removers.

http://www.cdc.gov
Address to the Centers for Disease Control

PRODUCT MANUFACTURERS

http://www.entitybeauty.com
This address will take you to one of the acrylic nail product manufacturers I mentioned earlier.

http://www.cnd.com
This address will take you to one of the acrylic nail product manufacturers I mentioned earlier. This company also offers a gel nail product.
http://www.nontoxique.com
A company providing top notch education and

holistic nail care products.

http://www.dazzledry.com
A company offering a number of products including nail lacquers which are DBP (Dibutyl Phthalate) and Toluene free.

http://www.masterworksbyamybecker.com
A wonderful gel line and education program opportunity by World Champion Amy Becker.

http://www.lightelegance.com
A full line of gel products including glitter gel, gel polish and as of January, 2013 an acrylic line.

nailcareinightmares.com

ORDER FORM

Online Orders: www.nailcarenightmares.com

Postal Orders: Lisa Ann Bowles
1466 Clovis Avenue
Clovis CA 93612

NAME:_____

ADDRESS:_____

CITY:_____St/Province_____ ZIP:_____

Telephone: _____

Email address:_____

SEND:

$24.95 plus shipping U.S. $5.05 for the first book, $3.00 for each additional book (same order).

Sales Tax: Please add 8.23% for books shipped within California.

Canada: $24.95 plus airmail delivery $7.50 for each book ordered.

Please make checks and money orders payable to:

Lisa Ann Bowles

nailcareinightmares.com

ORDER FORM

 Online Orders: www.nailcarenightmares.com

 Postal Orders: Lisa Ann Bowles
1466 Clovis Avenue
Clovis CA 93612

NAME:_____

ADDRESS:_____

CITY:_____St/Province_____ ZIP:_____

Telephone: _____

Email address:_____

SEND:

$24.95 plus shipping U.S. $5.05 for the first book, $3.00 for each additional book (same order).

Sales Tax: Please add 8.23% for books shipped within California.

Canada: $24.95 plus airmail delivery $7.50 for each book ordered.

Please make checks and money orders payable to:

Lisa Ann Bowles

nailcareinightmares.com

ORDER FORM

Online Orders: www.nailcarenightmares.com

Postal Orders: Lisa Ann Bowles
1466 Clovis Avenue
Clovis CA 93612

NAME:_____

ADDRESS:_____

CITY:_____St/Province_____ ZIP:_____

Telephone: _____

Email address:_____

SEND:

$24.95 plus shipping U.S. $5.05 for the first book, $3.00 for each additional book (same order).

Sales Tax: Please add 8.23% for books shipped within California.

Canada: $24.95 plus airmail delivery $7.50 for each book ordered.

Please make checks and money orders payable to:

Lisa Ann Bowles

FOR SUCH A TIME AS THIS...